MW00651178

DYNAMIC
CHRISTIAN
LIVING

PositiveAction
BIBLE CURRICULUM

Dynamic Christian Living

Written by Frank Hamrick with Champ Thornton

www.positiveaction.org

Third Edition 2010
Third Printing 2014

Printed in the United States of America

ISBN 978-1-59557-125-0

Edited by C.J. Harris and Kristi Houser
Design by Shannon Brown
Chapter Artwork by Del Thompson

Published by

CONTENTS

Birth: Salvation

Growth: The Bible

Breath: Prayer

Communication: Witnessing

Behavior: Daily Living

PREFACE

What are the most important factors that characterize a new physical life? The first one has to be birth itself. You cannot have a new life without a new beginning to life that we call birth. Second, the little newborn begins to receive nourishment and as a result begins to grow. Third, the little one is constantly breathing—taking in air and letting it out. Fourth, as the child grows, he begins to try to communicate with those around him, first through motions and facial expressions and eventually through words. Finally, the child develops a certain pattern of behavior based on his personality and how he responds to the actions of others.

These same five stages—birth, growth, breath, communication, and behavior—can be applied to the Christian. All five are essential to dynamic Christian living.

- Birth was used by Christ as a metaphor for salvation when He talked to Nicodemus about being born again in John 3.
- First Peter 2:2 reminds us that the way we grow spiritually is by feeding on God's Word.
- Prayer for the Christian is like breathing as he constantly communes with God (1 Thess. 5:17).
- Before returning to heaven, Christ commanded us to communicate the good news of salvation in Christ to the whole world (Mark 16:15).
- Being a Christian should affect everything about the way we live our lives so that even when we are eating and drinking—and in whatever else we do—we are doing it to the glory of God (1 Cor. 10:31).

This study focuses on these five areas. We call them the basics of the Christian life because they are the primary things that need to be present in the life of every believer. Therefore, they are also the first areas on which young believers need to focus. There are many Bible facts that you could learn this year, and there are many doctrinal issues you could discuss. But sometimes it's best to just go back and make sure you understand the basics and have made them part of your life.

Scripture Memorization Report Sheet

Week	Scripture	Due Date	Parent's Signature
1	John 3:18		
2	Ephesians 2:8-9		
3	Acts 16:30-31		
4	**Review**		
5	2 Timothy 3:16-17		
6	2 Peter 1:21		
7	Hebrews 1:1-2		
8	**Review**		
9	Psalm 119:9, 11		
10	Psalm 1:2		
11	Psalm 19:9-10		
12	**Review**		
13	John 14:13		
14	1 John 1:9		
15	Matthew 6:6		
16	**Review**		
17	2 Chronicles 7:14		
18	Matthew 6:9-11		
19	Matthew 6:12-13		
20	**Review**		
21	Romans 3:10-12, 23		
22	Romans 5:8; 6:23		
23	Revelation 20:14-15		
24	John 3:16		
25	Romans 10:9		
26	1 Corinthians 15:3-4		
27	**Review**		
28	Psalm 16:11		
29	Isaiah 55:2		
30	2 Corinthians 3:18		
31	Galatians 2:20		
32	1 Timothy 4:7		
33	Hebrews 12:1-2		
34	Acts 2:42		
35	**Review**		

BIRTH

SALVATION

Salvation is like birth. In fact, the Bible refers to salvation as the "new birth." When a man is saved, he is reunited with the source of spiritual life (John 10:10). He passes from a non-living state to life eternal (1 John 3:14). His new life in Christ gives him new desires for the things of God (Col. 3:1-2). This precious spiritual life begins to manifest itself in deeds of righteousness (1 John 3:7).

A new baby soon begins to desire all the things that other humans desire. His increasing activity attests to the fact that he is a living human being. So it is with the Christian. This "new birth" gives the believer new life, new desires, and new actions.

WHAT'S SALVATION ALL ABOUT? (PART 1)

TEACHER'S LESSON

- ***What Is Salvation?***
  - Salvation literally means to ________, to ________________, to ______________, to ________ or to __________________.
- ***Why Does Salvation Exist?***
  - God cares about man's ________
    - ______________ to sin
    - ________ and __________________
    - ________, __________, and ________
  - God cares about His _____________
    - Christ __________________________ to reveal God's glory
    - Christ ________________________________ to reveal God's glory
    - The cross of Christ reveals
      - The _________ of God that surpasses ________________
      - The ________ of God that surpasses ________________
      - The _________ of God that surpasses ___________
- ***How Is Salvation Provided?***
  - God's provision
    - A __________________ for the captives (Heb. 2:14-15)
    - A ____________________ for the condemned (1 Pet. 2:24)
    - A ____________ for the sick (Luke 4:18-19, 21)
  - Man's response

- ***What Are the Results of Salvation?***
  - ______________ instead of bondage
    - Freedom from sin's _____________
    - Freedom from sin's _________
    - Freedom from sin's _______________
  - __________ instead of weakness

WORD POWER

- *Repentance*—changing one's mind and actions
- *Faith*—complete reliance upon someone or something
- *Regeneration*—new and divine life given by God to those who believe upon the Lord Jesus Christ
- *Salvation*—deliverance from sin's penalty and power
- *Condemnation*—guilt and punishment for a crime committed
- *Substitute*—someone who stands in the place of another

STUDENT'S LESSON

To help us understand what salvation is all about, we will spend the first two student's lessons studying seven major terms that are associated with salvation—three in this lesson and four in the next lesson.

Repentance

The word "repent" means to change one's mind, thought, purpose, and views regarding a matter. It has the idea of turning away from going in one direction so that you can begin moving in the opposite direction.

Read 1 Thessalonians 1:9 and answer the following questions.

- To whom did the Thessalonians turn? ____________________________
- From what did they turn? ____________________________________
- Why did they turn? ____
  ____
- Which came first—turning to or turning from? ____________________

The order in which we find "turning to" and "turning from" is significant. Consider these three observations regarding the order in which we find the phrases "turning to" and "turning from" in this passage:

- A person may turn "from" sin without turning "to" the Lord. That is not repentance, but reformation. Many unsaved people do this in their lifetime.
- If a person turns "to" Christ, he will automatically turn "from" his sin.
- Thus, the emphasis in repentance is not so much on turning "from" sin as it is in turning "to" Christ. When a person is appropriately attracted to Christ, he will turn to Him in dazzled delight and will at the same time see his sin as odorous and repulsive! As the song writer said it,

  "Turn your eyes upon Jesus,
  look full in His wonderful face,
  and the things of earth will grow strangely dim,
  in the light of His glory and grace."

Read the following passages that teach us truths about repentance and answer the questions.

- Acts 20:17-21: What was the message Paul testified both to the Jews and also to the Greeks? ____

  ____
- 2 Peter 3:9: What is God's one desire for all men? ____________________

  ____
- 2 Timothy 2:25: How does one gain repentance? ____________________
- Luke 13:1-5: What will happen to all those who do not repent? ____________

  ____
- Acts 17:30: What is God's command to all men everywhere? ____________
- Romans 2:4: What can lead a man to repentance? ____________________

  ____

Faith

According to Acts 20:21, __________ is a counterpart to repentance. Though one must repent, he cannot do so apart from faith. Faith may be defined as "acceptance and complete reliance upon." If one does not exercise faith in Christ as Savior, he will not repent. Read the following verses and record the results of exercising faith.

- Acts 26:18, Romans 6:22 ______________________________
- Romans 5:1 ______________________________
- Galatians 3:26 ______________________________
- 1 Peter 1:5 ______________________________

Regeneration

Regeneration is God's giving us a new and divine life. Regeneration is given a special definition in John 3:3.

- What is it? ______________________________

How is regeneration described in the following verses?

- John 5:24 ______________________________
- 2 Corinthians 5:17 ______________________________
  ____

How are we "born again" or regenerated according to the following verses?

- John 1:12-13 ______________________________
  ____
- John 3:6-7 ______________________________
- James 1:18 ______________________________
  ____
- 1 Peter 1:23 ______________________________
  ____

WHAT'S SALVATION ALL ABOUT? (PART 2)

TEACHER'S LESSON

- ***The Necessity of Salvation***
  - God is ________, but man is a ____________
  - God lives in ____________, but man must go to ________
  - God __________ man, but man __________ God
- ***The Definition of Salvation***
  - _______________________ (John 3:3)—"__________________" or the __________________ whereby we pass from __________ unto ________
  - ___________________ (1 Pet. 1:18-19)—Christ paid the __________ of His blood to __________________us from the slave market of sin
  - __________________ (Heb. 9:22)—Our sins were __________________through the __________________of Christ's blood
  - ____________________________(Acts 13:38-39)—Through Christ, God __________________sinners to be _________________
  - _____________________________(2 Cor. 5:18)—Through Christ, sinners are ________________ to ____________________ or ______________ with God

WORD POWER

- *Righteousness*—conformity to God's holy standard
- *Remission*—the act by which something is laid aside or put away
- *Justification*—the act of being declared righteous
- *Redemption*—set free by the payment of a ransom
- *Forgiveness*—having one's sins cleansed and fellowship with God (or others) restored
- *Reconciliation*—restoration to friendship or harmony
- *Imputation*—giving the benefits or penalties of one's actions to another
- *Regeneration*—new and divine life given by God to those who believe upon the Lord Jesus Christ

STUDENT'S LESSON

In our last student's lesson, we studied three terms associated with salvation.

- What were they? ____

  ____

In this lesson we will study four more key salvation terms. (These terms have already been presented in the teacher's lesson.)

Redemption

Redemption means "to purchase or buy back." This term was used when a slave was bought from the marketplace.

From What?

- According to Titus 2:13-14, from what did Christ redeem us? __________

  ____

  (This means that redeemed people are not to continue in sin.)

- Why did He redeem us? ____

  ____

  ____

- Note that we were purchased for Him! We belong to Him. Salvation is *about* Him, it is *from* Him, and it is *for* Him.
- Are you redeemed? ______________________________
- Are you living up to His reason for redeeming you? ______________________________
____
- What did Christ do in order to redeem us? ______________________________
____

How?

- According to Galatians 3:13, from what are we redeemed? ______________________________
____
- Christ removed the curse by becoming a curse for us (He took our place). Where did He go that He might take our place? ______________________________

What's Changed?

- According to 1 Corinthians 6:19-20, what is your body after you are redeemed? ______________________________
- Who owns your body? ______________________________
- Why does He own it? ______________________________
- What should we do since we have been purchased by God? ______________________________
____

Remission

Remission means "to put away or to do away with." It has to do with God's putting our sins away.

What Did Christ Do?

- According to Luke 24:46-47, what did Christ do in order that we might preach remission of sins? ______________________________
____

- What is the responsibility of every Christian according to this passage?

  ____

Preaching repentance to all nations, however, is more than a "responsibility." It is a great privilege! We should be so thrilled and excited about this glorious Savior that we would want the whole world to know about Him!

What Does Man Do?

- Acts 2:38 was written to the Jews and explains what they had to do to receive the remission of their sins. What did they have to do? ______________

  ____

- Acts 10:43 was written for Gentiles (like Cornelius) and explains what we must do for the remission of sins. What is it? ______________

  ____

What Had to Happen?

- What had to happen that men might have remission (Heb. 9:22)?

  ____

- Whose blood do you think this verse is talking about? ______________
- According to Hebrews 10:17-18, how many times does a man have to have his sins remitted? ______________

Justification

Justification means "to declare one innocent or righteous."

How Is a Man Justified?

How are we justified according to the following verses?

- Galatians 2:16 ______________________________
- Romans 3:24; Titus 3:7 ______________________
- Romans 5:1 ______________________________
- Romans 5:9 ______________________________

What Are the Results of Being Justified?

What are the blessed results of justification according to the following verses?

- Romans 1:17 ____
- Romans 5:1 ____
- Titus 3:7 ____

How Much Does It Cost to Be Justified?

- According to Romans 3:24, how much does justification cost us?

  ____

Reconciliation

Reconciliation means "to restore friendship and harmony." It has to do with making peace with an enemy.

The Need for Reconciliation

- Why is reconciliation necessary? According to Romans 8:5-8, the carnal (fleshly, sinful, lost) man and God have what kind of relationship?

  ____

The Means of Reconciliation

According to Colossians 1:20-22, man was once alienated and an enemy of God in his mind. However, man can now have peace through the blood of His cross. Verses 21-22 tell us that He reconciled us in the body of His flesh.

- According to this passage, into what kind of people is God making the people He has reconciled? ____

  ____

To summarize, a person is saved by faith not by depending on works but by believing in Christ who died on the cross and shed His precious blood that we might be redeemed, justified, and reconciled.

Summary

Complete the following.

- In justification, I have been declared innocent or ____________________ .
- In redemption, I have been ______________________________________ by His blood.
- In regeneration, I have been ____________________________________ .
- In reconciliation, I have made ______________ with God.
- In remission, my sins have been ___________________________________
  ____ .
- All this happens when I exercise __________ in Christ and ____________ of my sins.
- Have you trusted Christ alone to save you from your sins? ____________
  ____
- Do you really know what salvation is all about? _____________________
  ____

WHAT MUST I DO TO BE SAVED?

TEACHER'S LESSON

- ***The Importance of the Question***
  - The present condition of man
    - The unsaved man—has no ______ or ________________________; is ______________ and ________________________
    - The saved man—is ____________, has ___________________________, and is ________
  - The eternal condition of man
    - The unsaved shall be _________________ in ________ (Mark 9:46)
      - ______________
      - ______________

The Man in Hell Has...

    - The saved will dwell in ____________ (John 14:2)
- ***The Answer to the Question***
  - What the answer is not
    - ____________________________________
    - ____________________________________
    - ____________________________________

- What the answer is
  - Believe = ____
    ____
  - Lord = _________________________
  - Jesus = ___________
  - Christ = ____

WORD POWER

- *Saved*—rescued from sin and judgment by Jesus Christ
- *Unsaved*—not rescued from sin and in danger of God's judgment
- *Baptism*—a church ceremony, instituted by Christ, in which a new believer is dipped under water to symbolize Christ's death, burial, and resurrection

STUDENT'S LESSON

- In Acts 16:30-31, the jailer asked Paul and Silas this question: ________________
  ____
- What was their answer? ____
  ____

What Does Not Save a Person?

According to Ephesians 2:8-9, Works Cannot Save

- Verse 8 says, "Not of ____________________." Verse 9 says, "Not of __________." What would man do if he could work and earn his salvation?
  ____

We have already learned that salvation is not ultimately for man's benefit but for God's glory! Thus, He designed salvation in such a way as to rob man of any glory he might desire and to bring Him ultimate glory.

According to Acts 10:1-2, 43, Fearing God, Giving Alms, and Praying Cannot Save

- What was Cornelius' rank? ____________________
- Was Cornelius religious? ☐ Yes ☐ No
- What does it mean when it says that he was "devout"? ________________
  ____
  ____
- Did Cornelius reverence or fear God? ☐ Yes ☐ No
- Yet Cornelius was not saved! He did not get saved until verse 43. What did Cornelius have to do to be saved? ____________________________

According to Acts 8:9-12, Baptism Cannot Save

- Philip the evangelist was preaching the gospel in Samaria. How does Acts 8:12 say that the people responded? ____________________________
- What happened to the people who had already believed Philip's presentation of the gospel? ____________________________________
- So what does a person have to do before he is baptized? _______________
  ____
- If belief (and therefore salvation) comes before baptism, then can baptism save a person? ☐ Yes ☐ No

What Does Save a Person?

Read Romans 10:9. According to this verse, a person must do two things to be saved. (Actually, the two come together as one in faith, but this verse breaks "faith" into two aspects.)

First, we must be willing to "confess" (admit) with our mouth that Jesus is Lord (the ruler, boss, and authority in my life).

Second, we must "believe" in our heart (from the depths of our soul) that God raised Christ from the dead (that is, He died for our sins, was buried, and arose for our justification).

- The last phrase of Romans 10:9 gives us proof of what will happen when we trust Christ as our Lord and Savior. What does it say will happen when you confess and believe? ____

- What do you think it means to trust Christ as Lord? ____________________

  ____

- Have you done this?____

Who Does the Saving?

The key to understanding salvation is understanding who does the saving. There are four possibilities.

1. God alone does the saving.
2. Man alone does the saving.
3. Man, with God's help, does the saving.
4. God, with man's help, does the saving.

- Jonah 2:9 says that salvation is of the Lord . Read Ephesians 2:8-9. Is salvation of man? ☐ Yes ☐ No

- What phrase proves this? ______________________________________

  ____

- According to these verses, salvation is a gift from God. Do you work for a gift? ☐ Yes ☐ No

- Verse 9 states plainly that salvation is not a work. Therefore, which of the four possibilities is the correct one? ________________________________

  ____

THE ASSURANCE OF SALVATION

TEACHER'S LESSON

- ***Test of ____________________ (1 John 2:3-5; 5:2-3)***
  - Assurance comes from keeping His ________________________ (2:3-5)
  - We obey because we ________ God (5:2-3)
- ***Test of _________***
  - Love not the __________________ (2:15)
  - Love the _______________________ (3:14)
  - Love ______ (4:20-21)
- ***Test of ______________***
  - Jesus is ________________________________ (4:2-3)
  - Jesus is ____________________ (5:1)
  - Jesus is ____________________________ (5:10)

WORD POWER

- *Believe*—to completely rely upon someone or something
- *Assurance*—the God-given confidence that you are His child
- *Obedience*—doing what pleases the Lord and keeping His commands
- *Love*—a heart-felt commitment to someone or something
- *Commands*—the laws or rules that God wants us to obey
- *Lust*—a strong desire
- *Confess*—to verbally acknowledge something to be true

STUDENT'S LESSON

Can a Person Know He Is Saved?

Can a person really know for sure that he is saved, or does he have to go through life hoping that he is saved?

Declared

- Why was 1 John written (5:13)? ________________________________
  ____

If a man cannot know whether or not he is saved, then the whole book of 1 John is worthless, for it was written that men might "know."

Illustrated

- Did Paul know he was saved (2 Tim. 1:12)? ☐ Yes ☐ No
- Of what was Paul persuaded? ________________________________
  ____
  ____
- Who does the keeping (protecting)—man or God? ________
- What had Paul "committed" to Him? ____________________________
- According to Job 19:25-26, did Job know he was saved? ☐ Yes ☐ No
- Job said that even though he would die, he would still ______________ .
- Can a person really know for sure that he is saved? ☐ Yes ☐ No
- Do you know for sure? ☐ Yes ☐ No

Does a Person Need to Know He Is Saved?

The Bible answers "yes" to the question, "Can a person know if he is saved?" But why does man need to know whether or not he is saved?

His Destiny Depends on His Salvation

Man needs to know because his soul's destiny depends on it. Whether or not a man goes to heaven or hell hinges on whether or not a man is saved.

- Should a man be uncertain about such an important thing? ☐ Yes ☐ No

His Service Depends on Salvation

Man needs to know because only saved people are supposed to serve God.

- According to Ephesians 2:10, a Christian is the product of whose workmanship? ______________
- Why (for what purpose or goal) did God "create" us in Christ Jesus?

  ____

  ____

If we don't know whether or not we are saved, then we don't know whether or not we are qualified to serve God.

His Joy Depends on His Assurance

Man also needs to know because it brings joy.

- According to Luke 10:20, what should be the thing that we rejoice about daily? ____

  ____

If a man could not know he was saved, then why did Jesus say to "rejoice" in the knowledge that our names are written in heaven?

How Can a Person Know He Is Saved?

Believers Keep His Commandments

- According to 1 John 2:3-4, a person who is saved will have a desire to

  ____ .

The commandments spoken of here are not the Ten Commandments of the Old Testament but the major New Testament commandments, which are named in 1 John 3:23.

- What are they? ____

____

____

Believers Live Righteously

- Who is born of Christ (1 John 2:29)? ______________________________

____

____

Those who are living in sin do not have this assurance. This is why Christians who get out of fellowship often begin to doubt their salvation.

Believers Have Love for the Brethren

- How do we know that we have "passed from death unto life" (1 John 3:14)?

____

____

- Do you like to be around saved people? ____________________________

____

Believers Have Assurance

- Christians can claim the assurance of God's promise. What does Romans 10:9 say a person has to do be saved? ____________________________

____

____

____

- What promise does God make at the end of Romans 10:9? ______________

____

____

- Can God lie? ☐ Yes ☐ No

- If you have genuinely done what Romans 10:9 says, then are you saved? ☐ Yes ☐ No

Important: The assurance of your salvation is not based on what you do or don't do but what you desire and don't desire! Believers will never perfectly keep God's commandments, nor will they live a perfectly righteous life or perfectly love each other. We are all imperfect beings. Yet, if we are truly saved, we will have a desire to know and obey God's Word. We will have a desire to live a righteous life (even when we sin), and we will have an attraction to believers more than an attraction to the unsaved.

- Do you know whether or not you are saved? ☐ Yes ☐ No

- How do you know? ____
  ____

ISRAEL'S AID
LOOK AT THIS PSALM
JOURNEY FOR ISRAEL'S
RAIN IN THE RAINY SEASON?
THIS IN ISRAEL, BUT

GROWTH

THE BIBLE

One sign of life is growth. When a new baby arrives, his desires are soon known to everyone in the household. His piercing cry attests to the fact that he is hungry. The young Christian also desires food after his "new birth," and that hunger should continue throughout his entire Christian life. First Peter 2:2 tells us that the Christian's food is the Bible. This new desire for the milk of the Word, when fulfilled, begins to produce growth. The amount of Bible that the Christian "eats" determines how much he will grow. Adults prepare good food for their children in order that they may grow and mature. So it is that the mature Christian who has begun to master the Bible in turn begins to feed others (Prov. 10:21).

GOD'S INSPIRED WORD

TEACHER'S LESSON

- ***How We Got Our Bible***
  - ________________
  - ________________
  - ________________
  - ________________
- ***What Is Inspiration?***
  - Defined
    - Revelation = ________________________________ of truth
    - Inspiration = ________________________________ of truth
    - Illumination = ________________________________ of truth
      - Inspiration means that ________ directed the writing of Scripture so that, without destroying the ________________________ of the human authors, the end result was the ________________, ____________________, ____________________ Word of God.
  - Described
    - Plenary = ____
    - Verbal = ____
    - Infallible = ____
    - Inerrant = ____
- ***What Does the Bible Claim to Have?***
  - Divine ________________________ (2 Tim. 3:16)
  - Divine ____________________ (John 12:48)

- ***Why Did God Give Us the Bible?***
  - To ____
  - To plainly ____________ Himself and His will to man
  - Three truths we learn only in the Bible
    - Man is totally ________________ (corrupt)—Isaiah 64:6
    - Man is ________________ to save himself—Romans 5:6
    - Man can only be saved by __________ in the finished work of Christ on the cross—Acts 4:12

WORD POWER

- *Bible*—the perfect, inspired record of God and His dealings with mankind
- *Revelation*—God displaying Himself through His actions or speech
- *Inspiration*—God breathing-out His Word to the biblical writers (through the Spirit) so that what they wrote was the Word of God
- *Authoritative*—requiring obedience
- *Illumination*—spiritually empowered understanding of Scripture
- *Infallible*—completely dependable and incapable of failing in its purpose
- *Inerrant*—free from error
- *Plenary Inspiration*—the doctrine that the entire Bible is inspired
- *Verbal Inspiration*—the doctrine that every word and detail of the Bible is inspired

STUDENT'S LESSON

Inspiration

In the teacher's lesson we discussed where the Bible came from. We saw that it originated in the mind of God and that He revealed it to men in such a way that what they wrote was completely reliable and without any mistakes.

In this student's lesson we will not examine what men have said about the Bible but what the Bible has to say about itself. What does the Bible claim to be? As you will see, the Bible makes two specific claims for itself. First, the Bible claims to be inspired by God. That is, it is God's word to man. Second, the Bible claims to possess God's authority. That is, it has the right to tell us how to live, and it is the standard by which we should measure our lives. Use the following clues to fill in the crossword below. These verses teach the two truths about the Bible that you just read about.

1. The opening verses of Isaiah record "the _____ of Isaiah."
2. According to 2 Timothy 3:16, all _____ is inspired (breathed out) by God.
3. According to 2 Peter 1:21, who guided and protected the men who wrote the Scriptures? _____
4. According to Galatians 1:12, Paul did not receive the gospel from _____.
5. Proverbs 30:5 says that _____ word of God is pure and true (tested).
6. In Galatians 1:12, Paul says that he received the gospel by _____ from Jesus Christ.
7. According to 1 Corinthians 14:37, Paul's writings were actually commandments from the _____.
8. According to Exodus 20:1, who spoke the Ten Commandments? _____
9. According to 1 Thessalonians 2:13, the Thessalonians received Paul's words as the _____.
10. Jesus said in John 12:48 that His Word would judge men in the _____.

What Is Inspiration?

The word "inspired" literally means "God-breathed." "Inspired" or "inspiration" in 2 Timothy 3:16 means the Scriptures were breathed into the hearts and minds of the biblical writers by God Himself.

- There are three ideas concerning inspiration.
    - One holds that some of Scripture is inspired.
    - Another says that none of Scripture is inspired.
    - A third states that all of Scripture is inspired.
- Which one does 2 Timothy 3:16 support? What in this verse shows that the other two views are wrong?

  ____

  ____

  ____

  ____

  ____

- According to 2 Timothy 3:16, for what four things are the Scriptures profitable? ____

  ____

So, taking each of the above words in succession, we can say that the Word of God shows the believer . . . (Fill in the exact word used in the verse.)

1. what is right (=teaching) "______________________________"
2. what is wrong (=turning) "______________________________"
3. how to make it right (=transforming) "______________________________

   ______________________________"
4. how to keep it right (=training) "______________________________

   ______________________________"

Who Wrote the Bible?

Human Authorship

- There were about 40 human authors who wrote the Bible. According to 2 Peter 1:21, they wrote as what happened? ____________________

  ____

Divine Authorship

- According to 1 Peter 1:10-12, about what did the Old Testament prophets prophesy? ____

  ____

  ____

  ____

  ____

- According to this passage, did the prophets understand everything about what they were writing? ☐ Yes ☐ No

- Write the phrase from this passage that proves your answer.

  ____

  ____

  ____

  ____

- According to Acts 1:16, who wrote Psalms (both the human and the divine author)? ____

  ____

- According to Acts 28:25, who wrote the Book of Isaiah? ____________

  ____

PROOFS FOR INSPIRATION

TEACHER'S LESSON

- ***The Testimony of ___________________________***
  - Christ ________________ the inspiration of the OT
    - Made specific statements about its ______________________ ____
    - Referred to its events as __________________
    - Believed His life was a _____________________ of its teachings
  - Christ __________________the inspiration of the NT
    - _______________(John 14:26)
    - ________________(John 14:26; 16:13)
    - ___________________ (John 16:13)
- ***The Self-testimony of____________________***
  - The specific ____________ of Scripture
  - The unique __________ of Scripture
  - The amazing ________________ of Scripture
  - The precious ________________________ of Scripture
  - The fulfilled _____________________ of Scripture
    - Over ________ Messianic prophecies fulfilled in Christ
    - _______ prophecies fulfilled in one 24-hour day
  - The powerful ______________ of Scripture

WORD POWER

- *Testament*—a covenant or agreement; the term used as the name for the two halves of the Bible (the Old Testament and the New Testament)
- *Prophecy*—a God-given forth-telling of truth (preaching) or fore-telling of the future (prediction)
- *Preservation*—the doctrine that God has worked to keep His Word from being lost or destroyed
- *Archaeology*—the study of the remains of past civilizations

STUDENT'S LESSON

Fulfilled Prophecy

Second Peter 1:19 says that prophecy is sure (certain, trustworthy, unchanging). Study verses 16-18. Here, Peter tells the reader that he was an eyewitness of Christ on the Mount of Transfiguration and that he also heard the voice of the Lord identify Jesus Christ as His own beloved Son. Yet, Peter says that prophecy is even more sure (verse 19) than what he saw and heard!

- So, which should be easier to believe—an incident that you actually saw happen or the inspiration of God's Word? ______________________________

  ____

There are over 1,000 predictions in the Bible of future events, and every one of them that relate to events up to the present time have been fulfilled. In Micah 5:2, we have a remarkable prediction about Christ.

- Write out the prediction in your own words. ______________________

  ____

Micah 5:2 was written about 750 years before Christ's birth. No man could have so accurately predicted such a birth!

- Who told Micah where Christ would be born? ______________________

No human could have made 1,000 predictions about the future and have all of them come true! Only a supernatural author could have done so. Therefore, fulfilled prophecy proves the inspiration of the Word of God.

- Match the following list of Old Testament prophecies with the New Testament passages in the chart below. In the right-hand column state the prophecy

Psalm 22:1	Psalm 22:18	Isaiah 7:14	Zechariah 11:12-13
Psalm 22:15	Psalm 34:20	Micah 5:2	Zechariah 12:10

N.T. Passage/O.T. Reference	***Prophecy***
John 19:37	
Matthew 27:5-10	
Luke 2:4-7	
Matthew 27:35	
Mark 15:34	
John 19:28-29	
John 19:31-33	
Matthew 1:21-23	

Mathematically speaking, it is impossible that all of these prophecies would come true. There are over 1,000 prophecies in the Bible. The chances of all 1,000 coming true are more than one in ten to the 300th power. Yet, all came true. Thus, it can be no accident. God must have written it.

Archaeological Confirmation

Every archaeological discovery of man has further displayed the Bible to be correct in every detail. Not once has man found the facts in God's Word to be incorrect. Many scientists and archaeologists have tried to find errors in Bible history. The more they discover, however, the more accurate they find God's Word.

Life Transformation

Transformed lives confirm the Word to be empowered by God. What does God's Word say it has the power to do (1 Pet. 1:22-23)? ______________________________________

____

We could list thousands of men whose lives have been completely transformed by the preaching of the Word. No natural book could make this claim.

Project

In our lesson this week we have been discussing why the inspiration of the Bible is important. Write a two-page paper about this topic. You will want to consider the following questions: (1) Why is the inspiration of the Bible so critical? (2) What evidences exist for believing the Bible is inspired? (3) What would be different if it were not inspired? (4) What effects are felt when people do not believe in the Bible's inspiration? (5) What effects are felt when people do believe in the Bible's inspiration? (6) How does believing in the inspiration of the Bible affect my life?

The Revelation
Psalms
Isaiah
The Gospel of Matthew
I Samuel
JOHN
GALATIANS
The Book of Exodus
The Book of Romans
HOLY BIBLE

LESSON 7

ONE BOOK OR MANY BOOKS?

TEACHER'S LESSON

- ***The Bible— __________ Book***
  - The Bible's ___________________ (Heb. 1:1-2)
    - Different time________________ (over 1500 years)
    - Different __________ (dreams, angels, oral communication)
  - The Bible's unity (only one Author)—___________________
- ***The Bible—_________ Books***
  - Old Testament
    - Threefold arrangement (____________ Bible)
    - Fourfold arrangement (Septuagint and ______________ Bibles)
  - New Testament
- ***The Bible—Two*** _________________________
  - Testament = _________________
  - Covenant = an ___________________ between two parties
  - Need for two covenants
    - The Old Covenant was limited
      - Because it was ________________—pointing to Christ
      - Because of its _____________—highlighting their sinfulness

- The New Covenant is superior
  - Because it is ______________________________—by having been fulfilled by Christ
  - Because it is ________________________—by Spirit-empowered obedience
- Necessity of the Old Testament
  - The Bible of our ________ and His ________________
  - The Old Testament is the ____________; the New Testament is the __________
  - Written for our ____________________ (1 Cor. 10:1-11)
  - Written to reveal God's _________ and _________

WORD POWER

- *Covenant*—an agreement between two individuals or groups
- *Torah*—the first five books of the Bible which were written by Moses; it is also known as the Pentateuch or the Law
- *Nebiim*—the prophetic books of the Old Testament
- *Ketubim*—a collection of 13 Old Testament books containing the poetic books, the "five scrolls," and the historic books
- *Megilloth*—contains five books of the Old Testament which were read aloud at various Jewish festivals; also known as the "five scrolls"
- *Old Covenant*—the agreement recorded in the Old Testament that God made with the nation of Israel making them His people
- *New Covenant*—the new agreement recorded in the New Testament that God has made with all who repent and believe on Jesus Christ, who has fulfilled all of the covenant's demands
- *Gospels*—literally meaning "good news;" the name given to the four books of the New Testament which portray the person and work of Jesus Christ
- *Epistles*—letters of the New Testament written to explain and apply the truth about Jesus Christ to Christian living

STUDENT'S LESSON

What is this book we call "the Bible"? The Bible is the object of both criticism and debate in religious circles today. However, there are several things about which we can be certain.

- It is a collection of ____ books divided into the Old and New Testaments.
- There are ____ books in the Old Testament and ____ in the New Testament.

These sacred writings are called the Bible. The word "Bible" comes from the Greek word *biblios* and means "the books."

- The Bible is sometimes called "the Scriptures." This word comes from the Latin and means "the writings." What does Daniel 10:21 call the Bible?

  ____

The Bible is also called a two-edged or double-bladed sword (Heb. 4:12).

- Why do you think this term was used in referring to the Bible?

  ____

  ____

  ____

The Plan of the Bible

The Bible's Beginning

- The Bible begins with God. Write out Genesis 1:1. ____________________

  ____

  ____

The Bible's End

The Bible ends with God's grace to man.

- Write out Revelation 22:21. ______________________________

  ____

  ____

  ____

The Bible's Message

The Bible is a message from God to man, in which He reveals His glory and His offer of grace to mankind. But the Bible also instructs man in right living.

- Write out 2 Timothy 3:16-17 in your own words. ____________________

____

____

____

____

Do you see the connection here? In order to live the right kind of life you need to know more about God's grace and glory.

The Bible's Central Figure

- Christ is the central figure of the Bible. What does John 5:39 say that the Scriptures do concerning Christ? ____________________

  ____

- According to Acts 10:43, of what do the prophets all write?

  ____

  ____

- According to Acts 18:28, what do the Scriptures teach about Jesus?

  ____

  (Note: Christ means "anointed one" or one selected by God to be our Rescuer.)

- According to Luke 24:26 and 1 Peter 1:10-11, what two things do the Old Testament Scriptures teach about Jesus Christ?

  ____

  ____

- According to 1 Corinthians 15:3-4, what do the Scriptures teach about Christ?

  ____

  ____

- In your own words, what is the plan of the Bible?

  ____

  ____

  ____

  ____

The Bible's Central Message

The Bible Was Written to Reveal the Glory of God

Sadly, we often read God's Word and see everything but the glory of God. The reason is because we have a wrong mindset when we approach the Bible. We think that the Bible is merely God's book of instructions for us. We believe the Bible to be primarily our life manual.

But this misses the main purpose and tends to blind us to the greater glories and truths of God's Word. God's Word is not about *us*, but about *Him*. It is His self-revelation of *His glory and grace*. This is why Genesis 1:1 begins with God.

In John 5:39, Jesus admonishes the Jewish leaders of His day who were diligently searching the Scriptures because they think that by knowing and obeying the laws of Scripture they will be saved. He then reminds them that the Scriptures speak of Him, the only true means of salvation. The Pharisees erred in treating the Bible as a manual for living rather than as a revelation of Jesus Christ.

In 2 Corinthians 3:18, Paul reminds the Corinthian believers that if they would think about the glory of God as revealed in the Scriptures, they would be transformed. Again, this shows us that God's Word is designed to reveal His glory.

- Name three things the Bible teaches about God's glory. ________________
  ____
  ____

The Bible Was Written to Reveal the Grace of God

The Bible closes with these words, "The grace of our Lord Jesus Christ be with you all" (Rev. 22:21).

Between Genesis 1:1 and Revelation 22:21 we find two major themes: God's glory and God's grace. And God's glory is best seen in His grace—especially in the giving of His Son to die for the sins of men. Nowhere in all the annals of history is there a greater demonstration of the glory and grace of God than in the Cross.

- Give three evidences of God's grace from the Bible. ________________
  ____
  ____

WHICH BOOKS ARE INSPIRED?

TEACHER'S LESSON

- ***The Apocrypha***
  - Its meaning: ____________ or ______________
  - Its description
  - The question of its inspiration
- ***The Canon***
  - Its meaning: ____________________________
  - Its relationship to ______________________
  - Its development
    - The Old Testament canon
      - The process
      - The history
      - Scriptural evidence (Luke 11:51, 24:44)
    - The New Testament canon
      - Apostolic ___________________
      - Widespread ___________________
      - Biblical ___________________
      - Divine ___________________
- ***Adding to or Subtracting from God's Word***
  - We add to God's Word by ____________________ it
  - We take from God's Word by _______________________ it

WORD POWER

- *Bible*—the perfect, inspired record of God and His dealings with mankind
- *Revelation*—God displaying Himself through His actions or speech
- *Inspiration*—God breathing-out His Word to the biblical writers (through the Spirit) so that what they wrote was the Word of God
- *Canon*—collection of 66 Bible books which God has inspired
- *Apocrypha*—books written during the period between the Old and New Testaments which are not inspired by God and not accepted into the canon
- *Septuagint*—Greek translation of the Old Testament; this translation was used by Jesus and many others in the first century
- *Apostolic*—related to the apostles or having their authority or approval
- *Providence*—God's guidance of all things in nature and human history according to His plans

STUDENT'S LESSON

We have surveyed some of the reasons why we believe the Bible is inspired. However, it is one thing to say that we believe the Bible is inspired by God, but it is something else to prove that we believe it by the way we live our lives. Thus, let's examine three specific ways in which we can prove we believe the Bible is inspired not only by logical reasons but also by living reality.

By Delighting in It

First, we prove we believe the Bible is inspired by delighting in it.

- Read Psalm 1:1-2 and write it out in your own words.

  ____

  ____

  ____

  ____

The word "delight" in verse 2 is the translation of the Hebrew word that means "to desire a valuable object." Do you value the Word as a great treasure—because it reveals the God who is the Treasure? Do you love its pages—because they tell you more about your Lord? Do you delight in studying God in the Word? Does it excite you to read about Him? God says that the man who has this kind of heart is the "blessed" man, and whatever he does will prosper with the Lord's blessing.

By Devouring It

Second, we prove we believe the Bible is inspired by devouring it.

- Read Jeremiah 15:16 and write it out in your own words.

  ____

  ____

  ____

Jeremiah sets an excellent example for us. We should so hunger for the Word that we literally want to devour it. How hungry are you for this fantastic book about our fantastic God? Think of it, the Bible is a special message from and about the God of the universe. It should be read, studied, memorized, and devoured as if we had come home to a delicious feast after a long exhausting day. It's the nourishment you need spiritually!

To use a different illustration, when archaeologists find a piece of rock with words written on it, they spend hours removing it, being careful to photograph it as it was found before extricating it from the ground. Then they take a fine brush and tediously brush away the sand and dirt. Next it is photographed again using regular photography as well as infrared photography. Finally, scholars around the world spend hundreds of hours pouring over every word and letter. Yet all they may be looking at is a copy of an ancient receipt or bill of sale.

In the Bible, we have something a million times more valuable. We have the authentic Word of the Creator of the universe in our hands. What do we do with it? Do we listen attentively when it is preached? Do we really know what it means to devour the Word of God?

By Declaring It

Third, we prove we believe the Bible is inspired by declaring it.

- Read Psalm 96:3 and write it out in your own words.

  ____

  ____

God's Word is too precious to keep to ourselves. In the illustration we used about the archaeologist, when he has finally completed his work on an ancient inscription, he publishes his findings in a book so that everyone will know about his new discovery. Do we not have something so much more important to declare? Why should we be ashamed to tell others? We have the greatest discovery, the greatest document, and the greatest doctrine in the world. Are you proving that you believe the Bible by sharing it with others?

If you are not sharing the gospel with others, don't start by simply deciding to try harder. Start, instead, by asking God to help you believe and love the Bible and its good news more. This will give you the motivation needed to faithfully fulfill the command. You never read the apostle Paul telling believers in his letters to share the good news. Why? Because that should be our natural response when we are believing and loving God and His Word. So, by all means, share the good news, but don't do it because you have to. Share the gospel because you love God and His Word so much! This is exactly how Paul himself operated in his ministry.

- Read 2 Corinthians 4:13. What were the two "steps" or the sequence in Paul's ministry according to this verse?

  1. ______________________________

  2. ______________________________

CAN WE TRUST THE BIBLE?

TEACHER'S LESSON

- ***Where Are the Original Manuscripts?***
  - We do not have __________________ of the originals because the ________________ on which they were written has ____________________________.
  - Why did God not allow the originals to be preserved? He knew that they would be __________________ (2 Kings 18:4).
- ***Can I Trust the Copies of the Original Manuscripts?***
  - Scribal ________________—They counted every ____________, and if they made one ________________ they would start over.
  - Manuscript __________________
    - Old Testament – In Isaiah 53 there is only ____ word (____ letters) in question after __________ years of copying.
    - New Testament

	Homer's ________	*New Testament*
Written	900 BC	
Manuscript copies	643	
Lines	15,600	
Lines in doubt	764	
% lines in doubt	4.9%	

- ________________ acknowledgment (Matt. 22:31-32, 45; John 10:34-35; Gal. 3:16)

- ***Can I Trust My Bible?***
  - Just because the Bible refers to ______________________ does not mean that they were ________________.
  - If God cared enough to __________ a book for us, He also cared enough to ________________ it.
  - If God created all ____________________________, He designed them to be translatable into ____________________________ with accuracy.

WORD POWER

- *Preservation*—the doctrine that God has worked to keep His Word from being lost or destroyed
- *Original Manuscripts*—the original documents penned by the biblical authors
- *Manuscripts*—hand-written copies of old documents, specifically those which contain part or all of the Scriptures
- *Transmission*—the copying and passing down of biblical manuscripts through history
- *Scribe*—a person who hand-copied and studied the Old Testament Scriptures

STUDENT'S LESSON

- What did Jesus say about the authority of Scripture (John 10:35)?

  ____

  ____

- What did Jesus say about the authority of His own words (Matt. 24:35)?

  ____

  ____

- According to John 20:31, why was John's Gospel written? ________________

  ____

____

____

- This lesson deals with the authority of the Word of God. What do you think "authority" means as related to God's Word? ______________________________

____

God's Word Is Our Final Authority for...

The Creation of the Universe

- Evolutionists call creation a myth. According to 2 Peter 3:5, what does God say about people like the evolutionists? ______________________

  ____

  ____

- Of what are they ignorant? ______________________________

- Who saw the beginning of the universe? ______

- Who is the only person qualified to tell about it? ______

Man's Problems

- Sociologists tell us that there are a number of reasons for man's problems today: poverty, illiteracy, prejudice, environment, poor housing, and unequal opportunity. Are these problems outward or inward? ______________

- Thus, if these sociologists are right, what is the answer to each of these problems? ______________________________

- According to the Bible, however, are man's problems outward or inward (Matt. 15:18-20)? ______________

- According to these verses, where do murders and lies originate?

  ____

- If the Bible is correct, then what must be done to correct man's problems?

  ____

- Which of the following is the best answer to man's needs today?

  - [ ] Feeding the world the Word of God
  - [ ] Feeding the hungry
  - [ ] Cleaning up the environment
  - [ ] Improving housing
  - [ ] Eliminating poverty
  - [ ] Finding cures for diseases
  - [ ] Signing peace treaties
  - [ ] Ending corruption in government

- Why did you choose this one as the best answer?

  ____

  ____

Christian Conduct

- Today the world's philosophy is: "Do your own thing." Does the Christian have the right to do whatever he pleases? ☐ Yes ☐ No
- Why or why not? ______________________________

  ____

According to the following verses, how is a Christian to live?

- Ephesians 6:11 ______________________________

  ____

- James 1:22 ______________________________

  ____

- 1 John 1:7 ______________________________

  ____

On what basis will God judge us?

- John 12:48 ______________________________

  ____

- Romans 2:2 ______________________________

  ____

- Romans 2:16 ______________________________

  ____

What questions about life do you have? What problems do you need solutions for? What guidance do you need as you make decisions about how to live your life? The answers you need are all found in God's Word, and you can find them there as you make it the final authority for your life

SYMBOLS OF THE BIBLE (PART 1)

TEACHER'S LESSON

- ***A Mirror***
  - ________________ us
  - ______________ us
    - Into _______________
    - Into _________________
  - _______________________ us
    - Through ___________________on God
    - By the _______________of God
- ***A Lamp***
  - ______________ in the darkness
  - ______________ the believer
- ***Water***
  - __________________ the life
    - Because it is _________
    - When it is _______________
  - Sustains ___________, ______________, and _________________
    - ___________________ (Rom. 1:13)
    - ___________________ or fruit of the Spirit (Gal. 5:22-23)
    - _______________ (Rom. 6:20-22)

- ***A Sword***
  - Maker and owner— ______________________ (Eph. 6:17)
  - Nature (Heb. 4:12)
    - __________
    - Powerful in ________________ and ____________________
    - Sharp : It ______________ and ________________
  - Use
    - Against __________
    - ______________ men

WORD POWER

- *Blessed*—happy or joyful; the characteristic of a life lived under the smile of God
- *Symbol*—something that stands for or represents something else

STUDENT'S LESSON

The Bible Is like a Mirror

- Read 2 Corinthians 3:18 and James 1:22-25. Both of these passages compare the Bible to a ____________.

The 2 Corinthians 3 passage speaks of the mirror as revealing the glory of God, while the James 1 passage speaks of the mirror as revealing the sinfulness of man. Both are right. When we look into God's Word, we see both the glory of God and the wickedness of mankind.

It Reveals God's Glory (2 Cor. 3:18)

In previous lessons we have seen that the Bible begins with God and ends with His grace (Gen. 1:1; Rev. 22:21). The purpose of everything God does is ultimately reveal His glory.

- Why are we saved (Eph. 1:6, 12, 14)? ______________________________

  ____

- Why did God create the nation of Israel (Isa. 43:7)? ________________

  ____

- Why does God do anything (Isa. 48:11)? __________________________

  ____

- What did the Psalmist seek in the Word (Ps. 119:9-10)? _____________

- What did Paul say we were to behold in the Word (2 Cor. 3:18)? ________

  ____

It Exposes Man's Sin (James 1:22-25)

- According to Hebrews 4:12, the Word reveals our ______________ and ______________. The Word reveals our secret sins.

- Why do men not want to read the Word (John 3:19-20)? _____________

  ____

  ____

Look at yourself in light of Ephesians 5:1-21.

- Name three ways God tells you to walk in this passage.

  ____

  ____

  ____

- Name six things we should avoid according to verses 1-7.

  ____

  ____

  ____

  ____

  ____

- List all the things we are commanded not to do in verses 8-21.

____

____

____

____

- How many of these are you doing? ____________________
- List all the things we are commanded to do in verses 8-21. __________

____

____

____

____

____

____

- How many of these are true of you? ____________________

The Bible Is like a Lamp

Read Psalm 119:105, 130 and Proverbs 6:23.

The Need

- Men who have never been saved dwell in darkness and cannot see the light of the gospel (2 Cor. 4:3-4). What does the Bible mean when it says that the gospel is "hidden to the lost"? ____________________

____

- The "god of this world" in verse 4 is Satan. What does this verse say he has done? ____________________
- Why then is it hard for the unsaved to understand their lost condition?

____

- What is the best thing one can do to open the eyes of the blind (the unsaved) and bring them to Christ? (Ps. 119:130; 2 Cor. 4:3-6) __________

____

The Instruction

Men who have been saved should walk in the light (1 John 1:7). That means to let God's Word be our constant instructor for every step we take. Read Psalm 37:23.

- How does God order our steps? ______________________________
- Can a person who never reads God's Word know God's orders?

  ☐ Yes ☐ No

The Bible Is like Water

Read Ephesians 5:25-27.

Declared

The Word is the agent which sanctifies and cleanses the church (God's people—Eph. 5:26).

Illustrated

- How were Christ's disciples "cleansed" (John 15:3)? ______________

  ____
- How can a young person cleanse his way (Ps. 119:9)? ______________

  ____
- What does "taking heed" mean? ______________________________

  ____
- What is God's way of keeping teens from sin (Ps. 119:11)? __________

  ____
- What is the best way to do this? ______________________________

- ***The Bible Is like a Sword***

Read Ephesians 6:17.

Illustrated

- The Word is a sword (Heb. 4:12) in the hands of a soldier of Jesus Christ (2 Tim. 2:3-4). We must be skilled in its use. What does 2 Timothy 2:15 say concerning this? Write this verse out in your own words.

  ____

  ____

- What did the "sword" do in Peter's hands (Acts 2:36-37)?

  ____

  ____

  ____

- What were the results of Peter's use of the sword (Acts 2:41)?

  ____

- What did the sword do to men's hearts in Acts 7:54?

  ____

- What were the results of Stephen's use of the sword (Acts 7:51-60)?

  ____

- When Christ comes back to earth, what will He do with the sword (Rev. 19:11-16)? ____

Identified

- According to Ephesians 6:17, the Word is called "the sword of the Spirit." Thus, who is best able to use the Word effectively—you or the Spirit of God? ____

- What does this teach us about being a witness for Christ?

  ____

  ____

SYMBOLS OF THE BIBLE (PART 2)

TEACHER'S LESSON

- ***A Hammer***
  - Used for ________________
  - Used for ______________________
- ***Gold***
- ***Fire***
  - ________________ the heart and life
  - ________________
- ***Seed***
  - Nature (1 Pet. 1:23-25)
    - _____________ -it is alive and abides
    - _____________
  - Work
    - Four kinds of soil
      - Wayside—__________ heart
      - Stony ground—_______ knowledge without ________ knowledge
      - Thorny ground—no ________; choked by...
        - Desires of the ________
        - Desires of the _______
        - ________ of life

- Good ground—__________ the Word, ____________the Word, and bears __________

- Planting of the seed (rules for the soul-winner)
  - _____________ the seed
  - __________________ the seed
  - ________________ the seed

WORD POWER

- *Zeal*—an enthusiasm or fire for something
- *Lust*—a strong desire
- *Conviction*—understanding of personal guilt
- *Parable*—an earthly story with a spiritual lesson
- *Meditate*—to consider carefully
- *Cultivate*—to encourage growth
- *Incorruptible*—never dying or decaying
- *Vow*—to commit to do something

STUDENT'S LESSON

- What four symbols of the Bible did we study in our last lesson?

  ____

  ____

In the teacher's lesson we studied four more symbols.

The Bible Is like a Hammer

Read Jeremiah 23:29.

The Need

- God describes men's hearts as __________ before salvation (Ezek. 11:19; Matt. 13:5-6, 20-21). Men's hearts must be ____________ so that the Word may be "planted," "take root," and "spring forth" into real salvation (Ps. 34:18; Acts 16:14).

- Often, the Word must be applied over and over again to bring a man to Christ. Does one blow always break a rock? ☐ Yes ☐ No
- What do you think this teaches you about witnessing? ______________

____

Read the following list, thinking about what the best way is to bring a man to Christ.

- Argue with him and prove to him that he is wrong.
- Treat him with kindness and never offend him or use the Word to show him he is a sinner.
- Pray for some tragedy in his life to wake him up.
- Hit him with philosophical, historical, and intellectual arguments.
- Give him the Word every chance you get.
- Which way is the best way? ______________________________

____

The Bible Is like Gold

Read Psalm 19:10 and 119:72.

- What is your attitude concerning wealth? ______________________

____

- What can earthly riches not do (Ps. 49:6-9; 1 Pet. 1:18-19)? ______________

____

- What happens to wealthy men and their wealth (Ps. 49:10)?

____

____

- When are riches helpless (Prov. 11:4)? ______________________

____

- What riches will endure forever (Eph. 2:5-7)? ____________________

____

How precious is God's Word to you? Answer the following.

____ 1. I study God's Word
(a) every day (b) some days (c) seldom (d) never.

____ 2. I (a) love (b) like (c) endure hearing God's Word preached.

____ 3. I spend at least (a) 5 (b) 10 (c) 15 (d) 30 minutes in God's Word each day.

____ 4. I memorize portions from God's Word at least
(a) once a day (b) once a week (c) once a month (d) once a year.

____ 5. I think about truths from God's Word
(a) every day (b) most days (c) some days (d) never.

____ 6. I use my Bible (or verses I have learned) in my conversations to others (Christians and non-Christians) to someone at least
(a) once a week (b) once a month (c) once every six months
(d) once a year.

- In light of your answers, how precious is God's Word to you?

____

The Bible Is like Fire

Read Jeremiah 20:9 and 23:29.

Illustrated

- Jeremiah was discouraged. He was through preaching and witnessing and vowed never again to open his mouth for God. Did he stick to his vow? ☐ Yes ☐ No

- Why not? ____

____

Applied

- What is the best way to have a heart that overflows to tell the gospel to unbelievers according to the above verses? ____________________________

____

If you refuse to obey and trust God's Word (and this includes evangelizing), your fire will go out. Two things keep a fire going—fuel and oxygen. The fuel of the Word of God stokes up the fire, but fuel without oxygen smothers the flame. The oxygen is obeying and trusting God's Word (including evangelism). If we don't live out what we take in each morning, we will soon smother the fire. Thus, evangelism, for example, without daily Bible study (oxygen without fuel) soon makes the evangelism cold and fruitless. Bible study without daily giving out the gospel (fuel without oxygen) soon makes one's Christian life dry and self-focused.

- Do you give out the Good News of the Lord? ☐ Yes ☐ No
- Do you study the Word daily? ☐ Yes ☐ No
- In what condition is your "fire" for the Lord?

  ____
- How will you stoke the fire of the Word of God? (List three practical ways you can stoke the fire today.)

  ____

  ____

  ____

The Bible Is like Seed

Read Isaiah 55:10 and Luke 8:11.

Described

Read the parable of the four soils in Luke 8:4-15.

- Of whom is the sower a picture? ______________________________

  ____
- What is the "seed"? ______________________________
- What act is pictured in "sowing the seed"? ______________________
- Name four places that the seed is sown.

  ____

  ____

  ____

  ____

- Who are those described as hard pathway hearers?

____

____

____

- Who are those described as shallow (stony) ground hearers?

____

____

____

- Who are those described as thorny ground hearers?

____

____

____

- Who are those described as good ground hearers?

____

____

____

Applied

We learn four lessons from this parable.

1. There will be no reaping without sowing (evangelism).
2. We should sow everywhere (on all types of ground).
3. It is the power of the seed not the method of presentation that does the work.
4. The ground should be prepared by the warmth of our love and the tears of our compassion (Ps. 126:6).

WHAT SHOULD WE DO WITH THE WORD?

TEACHER'S LESSON

- ________ ***the Word***
  - To receive a ____________
  - To receive ________________ of . . .
    - _______________
    - __________________
    - The _______________
- __________ ***the Word***
  - To learn more about ___________ (John 5:39)
  - For personal ___________________ (2 Tim. 2:15-16)
  - To discern __________ from error—as the ________________ (Acts 17:11)
    - Their _______________ —were eager minded
    - Their ____________________ —searched the Word daily
    - Their ________—desired to learn the truth
  - To be ready with ______________ (1 Pet. 3:15)
- ________ ***the Word***
  - Out of love for the ________ (John 14:23-24)
  - Out of love for the ________ (Ps. 119:163-168)
  - For __________________ (Ps. 119:9-10)
- _______________________ ***the Word (Phil. 2:16)***

WORD POWER

- ***Bereans***—the believers in Berea who evaluated Paul's teaching by studying the Scriptures
- ***Mystery***—a secret which must be divinely revealed to be understood
- ***Doctrine***—clear teachings of the Scripture
- ***Studying***—the slow, methodical examination of the Bible to gain understanding of its teachings

STUDENT'S LESSON

Many Christians have a desire to know the Word but never get around to really digging for its treasures because they don't know how. How many times have you sat down to study God's Word and after a few minutes were discouraged because you weren't getting anywhere? The problem is certainly a great one and must be overcome if you are to gain a clearer vision of our magnificent God. The following lesson should help you get started in the right direction. There is a secret to Bible study.

Have a Plan

We must have a definite plan of study. If you were to pick up a book—any book—and read pages 4, 35, 2, and 60 in that order, would it make much sense to you? ☐ Yes ☐ No

- Why not? ____

  ____

This is often the way we read God's Word. We do not have a plan. We do not go about our study systematically.

Study Words

For example, take the word *justified*. Read the following verses and note at least five things about justification: Romans 3:20; 5:1, 9; Galatians 2:16; 3:11.

- ____

  ____

- ____

  ____

- ____
  ____
- ____
  ____
- ____
  ____

Study Whole Chapters and Books

When studying a book, look for five things. (You can also do these for each chapter you study.)

1. Find the main idea of the book as a whole and of each chapter within it.
2. Outline the book as a whole according to how you think the book develops.
3. Find and underline the key verse in the book.
4. List what the book teaches about Christ.
5. List the ways the book applies to your life.

Look for God in the Word

Here is the key to all Bible study. The Bible is written to reveal the glory and grace of God. If you do not specifically look for His glory and grace in each passage read, you will miss the main thing in the passage. Thus, as you study . . .

Consider What the Passage Reveals About God

- What does God do in this passage?
- What does this passage reveal about what God is like (His attributes)?
- What does this passage teach me about how God acts (what He likes and doesn't like, how He responds in certain situations, etc.)

Consider What the Passage Reveals About Christ and the Gospel

- How does this passage communicate the good news of God's grace?
- What does this passage reveal about Christ (His action and attributes)?
- How is Christ pictured or prophecied in Old Testament passages?

Have a Question

We must not only have a plan, but we must have a question every time we read it. Listed below are ten questions that are necessary to have in mind every time you study the Word. Read John 13:36-14:6 and answer the following questions as you read.

- Who is speaking? ____

- To whom was the passage written or spoken? ____________________

  ____

- Under what circumstances were these words uttered? ______________

  ____

- What is the main idea of the passage? ________________________

  ____

  ____

- What does the passage teach concerning Christ or the Godhead?

  ____

  ____

  ____

  ____

- What does the passage teach about the grace of God?

  ____

  ____

  ____

  ____

- What is your favorite verse in this passage?____________________

- Is there an example for you to follow?_________________________

  ____

- Is there a promise for you to claim?__________________________

  ____

- Is there a sin for you to confess? ______________________________

____

- Is there an error for you to avoid? ______________________________

____

To give you more practice in Bible study, complete the following plan for the study of the book of 2 Timothy.

General Information

- Name of the book: ______________________________
- Author: ______________________________
- To whom written: ______________________________
- Main idea or theme: ______________________________

____

- Key verses: 2:3-4

Outline of the Book

1. The Charge to Guard the Gospel (chapter 1)
2. The Charge to Suffer for the Gospel (chapter 2)
3. The Charge to Continue in the Gospel (chapter 3)
4. The Charge to Proclaim the Gospel (chapter 4)

(outline from Guard the Gospel: The Message of 2 Timothy, by John R. W. Stott)

- What does the book teach about Christ or the Godhead?

____

____

____

- What does the book teach about the grace of God?

____

____

____

- How I can apply this book to my life?

____

____

____

Chapter Analysis

Chapter 1

- Main idea: ____________________
- Key verse: ____________________
- What it teaches concerning Christ: ____________________

  ____

  ____

Chapter 2

- Main idea: ____________________
- Key verse: ____________________
- What it teaches concerning Christ: ____________________

  ____

  ____

Chapter 3

- Main idea: ____________________
- Key verse: ____________________
- What it teaches concerning Christ: ____________________

  ____

  ____

Chapter 4

- Main idea: ____________________
- Key verse: ____________________
- What it teaches concerning Christ: ____________________

  ____

  ____

BREATH

PRAYER

What is prayer like? Prayer is like breathing! Real prayer originates with God (Eph. 6:18), just as breath does (Gen. 2:7). It is an ongoing, automatic response for every Christian (1 Thess. 5:17). It is a source of power and strength for the Christian (Eph. 3:14-20). Finally, prayer is God's method of eliminating sin from our lives (1 John 1:9), just as breathing eliminates poisonous carbon dioxide from our systems. Prayer, then, is like breathing. It is the breathing out of the soul upwards to God. It is a natural and necessary part of the Christian life.

WHAT IS PRAYER?

TEACHER'S LESSON

- ***Two ____________ of Prayer***
  - ________________ prayer
    - An act of _______________ (John 4:24)
    - For the _________________ (John 9:31)
    - Directed to the _____________ (John 16:23)
    - In the name of the ______ (John 14:13-14)
    - In the power of the _____________ (Eph. 6:18)
  - Quick __________________
- ***The ____________________ of Prayer***
  - ______________________: the act of rendering _____________ to God
  - ______________________: sins of the _________, _________, _________, ___________, ___________, and _________
  - ____________________________: giving thanks to God for His __________________ and __________________
  - ____________________________: for _____________ leaders, ____________________ leaders, your _______________, the _________, and __________________ requests

WORD POWER

- *Adoration*—loving, cherishing, and praising God, particularly for who He is
- *Confession*—admitting to and repenting of sin before God
- *Thanksgiving*—an expression of gratitude to God
- *Supplication*—telling God one's needs and asking for Him to meet them
- *Worship*—a personal response acknowledging and delighting in who God is
- *Revere*—to hold in high regard
- *Commune*—to fellowship with

STUDENT'S LESSON

This is the beginning of the third section in our study of the basics of the Christian life. First, we studied about the new birth. Next, we studied about growing in the Word. Now we begin a series of studies on the vital function of breathing—which in the spiritual life is prayer.

What Is Prayer

- Which of the following statements is the most accurate definition of prayer?

  ____

  - Prayer is asking God for things.
  - Prayer is our protection from trouble.
  - Prayer is communion with God.
  - Prayer is the best way to ease your conscience.
  - Prayer makes up for our sins.

Prayer is a two-way communication. Picture prayer as a telephone conversation. What kind of conversation would it be if only one party did all the talking, and all he ever did was ask for things?

Throughout Scripture, God's people offer His own words back to Him in prayer. David, Solomon, Nehemiah, Joel, Jonah, Mary, and Jesus (as well as those in the early church) all used and responded to Scripture in their prayers to God (for examples read Neh. 14:18; Jonah 4:2; Matt. 27:46; and Acts 4:24-30). When we read the Bible, God speaks. When we pray (in response to what we have read in the Bible), we speak to God in reply. Prayer is two-way communication.

- What does Psalm 85:8 say about this two-way conversation?

____

____

What Is Involved in Prayer?

Prayer is more than just saying a few words to God. It is more than a ritual. There are a number of elements involved in true prayer.

- Read the following verses and place them beside the statement or statements to which they apply.

A. Nehemiah 1:4	**E.** Matthew 6:9	**I.** John 16:23
B. Nehemiah 1:5	**F.** Matthew 6:11	**J.** Hebrews 4:16
C. Nehemiah 1:6	**G.** John 14:13-14	**K.** James 5:16
D. Nehemiah 1:8-9	**H.** John 15:16	**L.** 1 John 1:9

	☐ 1. Prayer is to be made to the Father.
	☐ 2.Prayer is to be made in the name of the Son.
	☐ 3.Prayer involves asking God for our needs.
	☐ 4.Prayer involves the worship of God.
	☐ 5.Prayer involves confession of sin.
	☐ 6.Prayer involves claiming the promises of God.

- Read through the above six elements again and place a check beside each area that you include in your prayers.

Who Can Pray?

What do each of the following verses say about who cannot communicate with God?

- Psalm 66:18 ____

____

- Proverbs 28:9 ____

____

- Isaiah 59:2 ______________________________

____

- John 9:31 ______________________________

____

- According to James 5:16 and 1 Peter 3:12, what kind of person can pray?

____

What Is the Point of Prayer?

Job makes a very probing statement about what some wicked people think about prayer. He asks, "What good is it to pray to God?" (Job 21:15). This raises a good question—If God is in control of all things, what is the benefit or point of praying at all? Isn't everything going to happen according to God's plan anyway (whether I pray or not)?

Why Should We Pray?

Read each verse below and give the reason we should pray.

- 1 Samuel 12:23 ______________________________

____

- Luke 18:1 ______________________________

____

- James 4:2 ______________________________

____

- Psalm 63:1-4 ______________________________

____

____

- John 14:13 ______________________________

____

____

____

____

Is Prayer Wrong

Some people say that prayer is wrong. Listed below are five objections to prayer. Using the following verses, answer each objection in your own words and write in the reference or references that best apply to each objection.

Psalm 14:1	Matthew 7:7-11	Psalm 106:44-46	John 14:13-14
Psalm 139:1-4	1 John 5:14-15	Matthew 6:5-8	

1. "There is no God, so why pray? You're talking to thin air."

   ____

   ____

   ____

   ____

2. "God already knows what will happen and controls all that will happen. So, there is no point in praying. Your prayers don't change anything—what God has planned out will happen."

   ____

   ____

   ____

   ____

3. "There is a God, but He is too high and too far removed to be interested in an insignificant thing like man. He will not pay any attention to you."

   ____

   ____

   ____

   ____

4. "God is immutable. He does not change. Thus, there is no need to pray since what will be, will be. Man cannot change an unchangeable God."

   ____

   ____

   ____

   ____

5. "God knows everything, so prayer is not necessary. He already knows what we need before we ask Him."

___

___

___

___

Prayer List Project

On a separate sheet of paper, make a prayer list using what you have learned in your lessons this week. Begin with a list of things for which you can give adoration to God. Then note any sins you need to confess to God. Next make a list of things you can thank God for providing. Finally, make a list of people and things for which you should pray. Then take some time to go to the Lord in prayer about the items on your lists.

THE IMPORTANCE OF PRAYER

TEACHER'S LESSON

- ***The ______________________ Regarded Prayer as an ____________________ Work (Acts 6:1-4)***
- ***Prayer Occupied a Prominent Place in ______________ Life (Luke 6:12)***
- ***Prayer Is an Important Part of ______________________ ____ (Heb. 7:25)***
- ***Prayer Is a Means of ______________ in a Believer's Life (John 16:24)***
  - Brings joy by _______________ what we need
  - Brings joy by _____________ us closer to God
  - Brings joy by _______________ God's love and grace
- ***Prayer Was a Key to Many of the Bible's ____________________________***
- ***Prayer Was Important in the Lives of God's ____________________________***
- ***Prayer Promotes _________________________________***
  - Exposes _______ (Ps. 51:2; 139:23-24)
  - Gives ____________(Eph. 1:16-17; James1:5)
  - Helps to overcome ________________ (Luke 21:34-36)
  - Gives ________ and __________for daily service (Eph. 3:16)

WORD POWER

- *Joy*—the delight that God gives His children

STUDENT'S LESSON

Prayer Is Important to Christ

Certainly any Christian would admit that prayer is important. Yet, many of us may not realize just how important it is. We trust that through this lesson you will gain a greater appreciation of prayer.

Christ Prayed

Note the hours and times of day that Christ prayed.

- Matthew 14:23 ______________________________
- Mark 1:35 ______________________________
- Luke 6:12 ______________________________

If prayer was so important to Christ, certainly it should be even more important to us.

Christ Spoke About Prayer

What did Christ say about prayer in the following verses?

- Luke 21:36 ______________________________
  ____
  ____
- Matthew 21:22 ______________________________
  ____
  ____

Christ Did Something to Make Prayer Possible

Read Hebrews 10:19-22 and answer the following questions.

- How can we enter the Holy of Holies? (By what means are we permitted to face the Father in prayer?) ______________________________

- What was the Old Testament way of approaching God?

  ____

  ____

  ____

- How was this new and living way opened up?

  ____

  ____

- Christ shed His blood that we might be able to ____________________

  ____

  ____.

- Christ did something else for prayer, according to Hebrews 4:14-16. According to these verses, who is our High Priest?

  ____

- Where is our High Priest? ____________________

- Why did our High Priest pass (ascend) into the heavens?

  ____

  ____

Prayer Is Important to God the Father

- Proverbs 15:8 states that the prayer of ____________________

  ____.

- First Thessalonians 5:17-18 states that prayer is ____________________

  ____.

Prayer Is Important in Daily Living

For what or whom should we pray according to the following verses?

- Matthew 5:44 ____

  ____

- Matthew 9:38 ______________________________

____

____

- Matthew 26:41 ______________________________

____

____

- Mark 11:24 & James 4:3 ______________________________

____

____

- Philippians 4:6 ______________________________

____

____

- 1 Thessalonians 5:25 ______________________________

____

____

- James 5:13-14 ______________________________

____

____

Project

Interview at least three Christians who have a testimony of being men and women of prayer. Ask them questions about how and when they pray. Find out what their prayer life was like as a teenager. Also, ask them to share some answers to prayer that they have seen in the past. Record a favorite answer or lesson you learned from the interviews on the lines below.

____

____

____

____

____

____

HOW TO PRAY

TEACHER'S LESSON

Prayer Should Be...

- ***Personal***
  - A personal ____________________
  - A personal _______________________________
- ____________________
  - A _________
  - A ___________
- __________________
  - __________________ distractions
  - __________________ distractions
- _______________________
- ***To a*** _______________
  - Not a ___________
  - Not a __________________________________
  - Not ______________
  - Not ___________
- ____________________________

WORD POWER

- *Persevere*—to continue in something until it is accomplished

STUDENT'S LESSON

Answer these questions based on what you have learned in the last few lessons.

- What is prayer? ____
- Who can pray? ____
- Why should a person pray? ____

  ____

  ____

This lesson is about the next logical question: How? Learning how to pray is necessary because . . .

Prayer Is Difficult!

Prayer Is Not Easy

- The disciples showed this when they made a request of the Lord in Luke 11:1. What was it? ____
- Another evidence of the difficulty of prayer is seen in Romans 8:26. In what way does this verse show us the difficulty of prayer?

  ____

  ____

Our Prayers Need Help

- According to the above verses, we have two who will help us to pray:

  ____

  ____

Learning to Pray

What Should Be Involved in Our Prayers?

Using Luke 11:2-4, let's see how Christ taught His disciples to pray. Beside each of the following elements of prayer write the phrase from Luke 11 that best expresses that element.

- Prayer is made to the Father: ______________________________

  ____

- Prayer involves worship of God: ______________________________

  ____

- Prayer involves asking God for needs: ______________________________

  ____

- Prayer involves confession of sin: ______________________________

  ____

- Matthew 6:9-13 also includes the model prayer given by Christ. What phrase in verse 10 shows an attitude of dependence on the Lord and of subjection to Him?

  ____

  ____

No one should pray without this attitude.

To Whom Should We Pray?

- Begin your prayer by addressing it to the Father. List three verses that prove this point. ______________________________

  ____

- Some address their prayers to Mary. Why do you think this is done?

  ____

  ____

- Does Mary have more influence over God than a Christian? ☐ Yes ☐ No

- What does Matthew 12:46-50 say concerning this? ____________________

____

- In John 2:4-5, did Jesus immediately do what His mother said?

____

____

____

- What words of Christ in John 2:4-5 prove this?

____

____

- In John 16:26-27, note Jesus' words about His praying to the Father. What do you think this means?

____

____

____

- Thus, we can see from this passage that we do not need to pray to Christ Jesus, and if this is true, certainly we need not pray to Mary. It may be permissible at times to pray to Jesus. What did Stephen pray in Acts 7:59?

____

- In 1 Corinthians 1:2, to whom did Paul say that all Christians—at least, when they called out for salvation—pray to? ____________________________

However, it certainly is not necessary to pray to Him. Jesus made it clear that prayer was typically to be addressed to the Father.

In Whose Name Should We Pray?

- According to John 14:13-14; 15:16; and 16:23, in whose name should we pray? ____

- What do you think praying in Christ's name means?

____

____

To pray in Christ's name means more than just saying, "In Jesus' name we pray" at the end of your prayers. In fact, saying these words doesn't mean that we really prayed in His name. To pray in His name means that we are asking God for the very things that we feel Christ would ask. We are asking in His name (with His approval). It means Christ is standing behind us in what we say and wants us to pray that way. It means also that if God answers our prayer, it will not be because of us, but because of His Son. We are coming to God on the basis of who His Son is and what He has done for us. Thus, it is good for every prayer to include words such as "in Christ's name we pray." But it is more than words; it is an attitude that is involved in praying in His name.

In Whose Power Do We Pray?

- According to Romans 8:26-27, who helps us to pray according to the will of God? ____________________
- According to Ephesians 2:18, by whom do we have access unto the Father?
  ____
- According to Ephesians 6:18, in whom are we to offer all our prayers?
  ____

Thus, we must be yielded and sensitive to the Holy Spirit when we pray.

HINDRANCES TO PRAYER

TEACHER'S LESSON

- ***Lack of ___________ (Ps. 66:18)***
- ***Lack of ___________ (Mark 11:24; James 1:5-7)***
- ***Lack of ___________ (Mark 11:25-26)***
- ***Lack of ___________ (James 4:2)***
- ***Lack of ___________ (James 4:3)***
- ***Lack of ___________ (Prov. 21:13)***
- ***Lack of ___________ (Prov. 28:9)***
- ***Lack of ___________ (1 Pet. 3:7)***

WORD POWER

- *Hindrance*— an obstacle that prevents something from working the way it is supposed to
- *Fellowship*—enjoyment of the relationship you have with God and other believers
- *Submission*—yielding to God as your authority
- *Compassion*—love and tender care

STUDENT'S LESSON

Prayer

This lesson deals with those things which hinder prayer. Certainly, since we have seen the important potential of prayer, we are concerned about avoiding things which would render our prayer life powerless. The following pitfalls should be avoided by every Christian teen.

Hindrances Identified

Identify the hindrances to answered prayer in the following verses.

- Proverbs 28:9 ____

  ____

- Isaiah 59:1-2 ____
- Matthew 6:5 ____
- Matthew 6:7 ____
- Mark 11:25-26 ____
- James 1:6-7; Hebrews 11:6 ______________________________
- James 4:3; 1 John 5:14 ________________________________

  ____

- 1 Peter 3:7 ____

  ____

Hindrances Explained

The First Hindrance

- In Proverbs 28:9, to what does the law refer? ____________________
- Thus, a Christian who does not ______________________________ will not have his prayers answered.

The Second Hindrance

- Why will God not answer a Christian who has sin in his life (Isa. 59:1-2)? ____

  ____

  ____.

- Therefore, what should a person do before his communion with God in prayer will be restored? ______________________________

The Third Hindrance

- According to Matthew 6:5, in what way can a person pray to be seen or heard? ____

  ____

- How do people do this today? ______________________________

  ____

The Fourth Hindrance

- In Matthew 6:7, what is vain repetition? ______________________

  ____

- How could the Lord's Model Prayer be prayed as a "vain repetition"?

  ____

  ____

The Fifth Hindrance

- Is there anyone you know against whom you are holding a grudge?

  ____

- What is your attitude toward your parents at this time? (Be honest.)

  ____

  ____

Check any of the following statements that reflect your attitude about your home and parents.

- ☐ I have no ill feelings of any kind toward my parents.
- ☐ I resent my mom.
- ☐ I resent my dad.
- ☐ I think my parents are too old-fashioned.
- ☐ I think my parents want what is best for me, but they don't honestly know what that is.
- ☐ My parents don't understand me.
- ☐ I get along great with my brother(s) and/or sister(s).
- ☐ I think my brother(s) and/or sister(s) are brats.
- ☐ I argue with my mom and/or dad a lot.

- [ ] I wish my parents would get lost.
- [ ] I love my parents, and we get along great.
- [ ] My home life is what a Christian home ought to be.

- My honest feelings about my parents and our home life are: ____ ____

- Will God answer your prayers based on your present attitude toward your parents?____ ____

The Sixth Hindrance

- According to James 1:6-7, what do you think it means to "waver" or "doubt" when you pray? ____ ____ ____

- On which point do you often waver when you pray: that He can answer your prayer or that He will answer it? ______________________

- Does God answer "yes" to someone who is not sure God will answer his prayer?____

The Seventh Hindrance

- According to James 4:3, what is James trying to keep us from doing in our prayers? ____ ____

Does God ever answer a prayer that is against His will? Let's see.

- In Numbers 11:4-9, how did the people feel about the manna? ____ ____

- What did they want in place of the manna? ______________________ ____

- Read Numbers 11:18-22, 31-34. Did they get their request?

  ☐ Yes ☐ No

- With what result? ____

  ____

  ____

- What does Psalm 106:15 say about this event? ______________________

  ____

  ____

- So does God ever answer prayers that are not in His will? ☐ Yes ☐ No

- With what result (as in Num. 11)? ______________________________

  ____

- What do you think the phrase in Ps. 106:15 means?

  ____

The Eighth Hindrance

- Could 1 Peter 3:7 also apply to a teenager and his parents? ☐ Yes ☐ No

- In what way? Defend and explain your answer.

  ____

  ____

  ____

  ____

- Read the heading for Psalm 51 and verse 4. Against whom had David sinned—God or other people? ______________________________

- In other words, your relationship to other people will affect your fellowship with God. So, if you sin against your parents, you are ultimately sinning against whom? ______________

- How will this sin against your parents, then, affect your prayers to and fellowship with God? ______________________________________

  ____

Hindrances Applied

- How many of the eight hindrances are in your life? List them below and spend the next few minutes in prayer dealing with these hindrances.

____

____

____

PREREQUISITES FOR ANSWERED PRAYER

TEACHER'S LESSON

- ***A Proper Relationship***
  - __________ (John 9:31)
    - Our ________________
    - Our ________________
  - ______________ (John 15:7)
    - In Christ
      - Results in bearing __________
      - Means being a ______________
    - In the Word of God
- ***A Proper Attitude***
  - ________________ (2 Chron. 7:14)
  - ______________________ (Luke 18:1-8)
  - ________________ (James 5:16)
  - __________ (James 1:5-7)

WORD POWER

- *Abide*—to remain in dependent fellowship with Christ
- *Prerequisite*—a condition that must be met before going further
- *Atonement*—Christ's sacrifice on the cross to pay for sin and to restore the broken relationship between man and God
- *Fervency*—passionate, focused devotion

STUDENT'S LESSON

This lesson deals with the requirements for getting an answer from God for our prayers. When the following eight prerequisites are met, every prayer will be answered by God with a "yes."

The Prerequisites

Identify the eight prerequisites for answered prayer by reading the verses below.

- Psalm 66:18 ____________________
- Matthew 18:19-20 ____________________
- Matthew 21:22 ____________________
- John 9:31 ____________________
- John 14:13 ____________________
- John 15:7 ____________________
  ____
- 1 John 3:22 ____________________
  ____
- 1 John 5:14 ____________________

The Answer

Tell whether each of the following statements is true or false. If the statement is false, tell why it is false.

☐ True ☐ False God will answer every prayer prayed in faith.

____

____

____

☐ True ☐ False God will not answer the prayer of an unsaved person.

____

____

____

☐ True ☐ False According to Psalm 66:18, if a person has sin in his life, even though he does not know it, his prayer will not be answered.

____

____

____

☐ True ☐ False A man who keeps the Ten Commandments will have his prayers answered with a "yes" according to 1 John 3:22.

____

____

____

☐ True ☐ False A man must meet all eight prerequisites to get a consistent "yes" answer from God.

____

____

____

☐ True ☐ False The most important part of prayer is to get a "yes" answer from God.

____

____

____

☐ True ☐ False God will answer with a "yes" the prayer of a man who is not in God's will but who prays for something in God's will.

____

____

____

LORD, TEACH US TO PRAY

TEACHER'S LESSON

- ***Introduction***
  - Purpose of the Lord's Model Prayer—teach us ________ to pray
  - Outline
    - Invocation—"Our ____________ in heaven"
    - Petitions concerning ______
      - God's name—"Cause Your name to be __________________."
      - God's kingdom—"Cause Your kingdom to ________."
      - God's will—"Cause Your will to be ________."
    - Petitions concerning ______
      - For sustenance—"Give us our _________ for today."
      - For forgiveness—"_____________ us our debts."
      - For deliverance—"Deliver us from the ________ one."
    - Doxology—"Yours is the ______________, __________, and __________."
  - Lessons
    - This prayer is only for ______________________.
    - God places great importance on ___________________.
    - The Lord's Model Prayer is comparable to the ________________ .
      - Part 1 deals with relationship to ______.
      - Part 2 deals with relationship to ______.
    - We need positive __________________________ on how to pray.
    - We can test our own ____________________________________ .

- There are certain ______________ to avoid in our prayer lives.
- Prayer is to begin and end with a recognition of ____________________.

- ***Our Father in Heaven***
  - What it means
    - Our Father—God's ________________ and __________
      - As a Christian, God is my Father by _______________ and by _______________.
      - Adoption means God has declared me to be one of His __________________ with ____________________________ in His family.
    - In Heaven—God's ____________ and ______________
  - What it teaches me about prayer
    - Prayer is to be __________________ to God the ____________.
    - Begin your prayers by reminding yourself of ____________________ and _______________________.
    - True prayer combines __________________ and ______________________ in a proper balance.

WORD POWER

- ***Adoration***—the act of rendering honor to God
- ***Confession***—admitting to and repenting of sin before God
- ***Thanksgiving***—an expression of gratitude to God
- ***Supplication***—telling God one's needs and asking for Him to meet them
- ***Invocation***—the act of calling on God in prayer, typically at the beginning

STUDENT'S LESSON

In Lesson 13 we discussed the four major aspects of prayer using the acronym ACTS. Now we are ready to look at them in greater detail.

Adoration

Adoration is the act of rendering honor to God. It includes the attitudes of reverence, esteem, and love.

- If adoration is the first part of prayer, what then should we do at the beginning of our prayers? ____

  ____

- The opposite of a prayer of adoration is a selfish prayer. Who prayed a selfish prayer in Genesis 28:20-21? ______________

- Why was this a selfish prayer? ____

  ____

  ____

  ____

  ____

Sometimes we act the same way. Instead of praising God for who He is, we promise to serve the Lord only if He will give us our selfish desires.

True prayer focuses on the greatness of God's attributes—the characteristics of God that describe who He is and what He is like. How is this seen in the following verses?

- Job 42:1-6 ____

  ____

- Isaiah 6:1-5 ____

  ____

- Daniel 9:3-4 ____

  ____

  ____

No one would go charging into the White House yelling, "Hi, Prez!" On the contrary, if we were about to be introduced to the President of the United States, we would wait anxiously in the waiting room, our heart pounding. When we met him, we would be careful about what we said and how we acted. Should we not be even more conscious of the greatness of our God when we come into His presence? Never should we rush into

God's throne room. We should begin our prayers by taking time to be in awe of God's greatness and majesty.

Confession

The second step in true prayer is confession of our sins. As we see God in all of His greatness, we then become aware of our own sinfulness and cry out as Job and Isaiah did. Read Job 42:6 and Isaiah 6:5.

Confession of Sin Honors God

Confessing sin honors God in the following ways.

- It honors His omniscience because it is admitting what He already knows.
- It honors His justice because it recognizes that God punishes sin.
- It honors His holiness because it realizes that God hates sin.
- It honors His mercy because it believes God will forgive sin.

Unconfessed Sin Robs a Believer of the Power of God

- According to Isaiah 59:1-2, why did Isaiah say that the Israelites' prayers were not being answered? ____

  ____

Confession of Sins Brings Answer to Prayer

In the following verses, who got an immediate answer to prayer after he confessed his sins?

- Daniel 9:20-23 ____________

- Luke 15:18-20 ________________________

Thanksgiving

- In Philippians 4:6, Paul commands us to ______________________ as we pray.
- Hebrews 13:15 commands us to offer what kind of sacrifice continually to God?

  ____

- For what did David offer praise to God in 1 Chronicles 16:8-36? (For the reason, see 16:1.) ____

  ____

- In Ezra 3:11, why did the people shout, praise, and give thanks to the Lord?

  ____

  ____

- For what did Jesus thank the Father in John 11:41? ____________________

  ____

- Complete the following lessons about thanksgiving based on the verses given.
  - Thanksgiving (praise) is one of the reasons God s______________ us (Eph. 1:6, 12, 14).
  - Thanksgiving (praise) is a form of w_______________(2 Chron. 7:3).
  - Thanksgiving is part of the w_________________ of God for our lives (1 Thess. 5:18).
  - Thanksgiving is a sign of the filling of the S_________ (Eph. 5:18-20).
  - Thanksgiving will be our eternal activity in h________ (Rev. 7:9-12).

Supplication

Supplication is asking God for specific needs and desires.

God Commands Us to Ask

We have emphasized that it is wrong for us to come to God in prayer just to ask Him for our selfish desires. But this does not mean that it is wrong to ask God for things when we pray. Our prayers should begin with adoration, confession, and thanksgiving; but they should also include supplications.

- Which verses in the following chapters contain a command for us to ask God for things in prayer? Matthew 7: ____ and Luke 11:____

- Which verses in the following chapters contain promises that are an encouragement for us to ask God for things in prayer? John 15:____; 16:____, ____, ____.

God Wants to Hear Specific Requests

Who prayed in the following passages, and what specific requests did they make?

- Numbers 12:10-13 ____
  ____
- Judges 16:27-30 ____
  ____
- 1 Samuel 1:9-11 ____
  ____
- 1 Kings 3:6-9 ____
  ____
- James 5:17-18 ____
  ____
  ____

God Delights in Answering Our Prayers

- According to John 16:26-27, why did Jesus encourage His disciples to pray to the Father? ____
- How are these verses an encouragement for you to pray and make requests of your Father?____
  ____

GOD'S NAME, GOD'S KINGDOM, GOD'S WILL

TEACHER'S LESSON

- ***Hallowed Be Thy Name***
  - What does "hallowed" mean?
    It means to ______________, ________________, honor, or treat with reverence and ______________.
  - What does it mean to hallow God's "name"?
    - Two interpretations
      - To honor God in relation to some specific ______________ of His character
      - To honor God in the use of His __________
    - Two implications
      - The most important thing in life is that God be ___________ and ______________
      - To ask for God's name to be glorified is to ask that He be honored throughout the whole _________
  - How can I sanctify God's name?
    - In my _________ (by worshiping God)
    - In my ___________ (by exalting God)
    - In my _______ (by serving God)

- ***Thy Kingdom Come***
  - ______________________ kingdom—God rules over ________ things
  - ____________________________ kingdom—Christ will rule over this ___________________
  - _______________________ kingdom—God rules in the ___________ of those who trust Him

A.D. 27	*Today*	*Future*
Interpretation	***Application***	***Consummation***
Earthly Kingdom	Universal Control Individual Commitment	Millennium Eternity
Initiation of the Kingdom	Extension of the Kingdom	Manifestation of the Kingdom

- ***Thy Will Be Done***
  - What is God's will?
    - We cannot come to know the ________ of God apart from knowing the ________ of God.
  - Why should I pray for God's will to be done?
    - Because His ___________________ is not always done on earth
    - Because He uses ________ to demonstrate His___________
  - How may I practice this petition in my prayer life?
    - God allows disobedience to His desires in order to teach me the emptiness of a ____________________ life.
    - True prayer results in my _____________ being ____________________ to God's desires.

WORD POWER

- *Universal Kingdom*—God's authoritative rule and reign over all things
- *Eschatological Kingdom*—Christ's end-time rule of the earth
- *Soteriological Kingdom*—God's rule in the hearts of all believers
- *Reverence*—to hold something in high regard
- *Consummation*—the climax or goal toward which everything is heading

STUDENT'S LESSON

God's Name

We learned in the teacher's lesson that it is very important for us to "hallow" (honor) God's name and that one way we can do that is to remember the names for God in the Bible and to treat Him with reverence because of what His names mean.

Read the verses that contain the following names for God. Then tell what each name means. These are all compound names for God—names combined either with el (the Hebrew word for god) or Jehovah (the name translated as "the LORD").

- *El Elyon* (Genesis 14:20): the M______ H______ God
- *El Roi* (Genesis 16:13-14): the God who s______
- *El Shaddai* (Genesis 17:1): A______________ God
- *El Olam* (Genesis 21:33): the e____________________ God
- *Jehovah-jireh* (Genesis 22:14): the Lord will p____________
- *Jehovah-rapha* (Exodus 15:26): the Lord who h________
- *Jehovah-nissi* (Exodus 17:15): the Lord is my b__________
- *El Hay* (Joshua 3:10): the l__________ God
- *Jehovah-shalom* (Judges 6:24): the Lord is p________
- *Jehovah-raah* (Psalm 23:1): the Lord is my s______________
- *Jehovah-tsidkenu* (Jeremiah 23:6): the Lord our r________________________
- *Jehovah-sabaoth* (Jeremiah 31:35): the Lord of h________
- *Jehovah Shammah* (Ezekiel 48:35): the Lord is t______

God's Kingdom

In the teacher's lesson we discussed the three major ways in which the term "kingdom" is used in Scripture. It is used to refer to God's universal, eschatological, and soteriological kingdoms. As a review of the differences among these three, tell which aspect of God's kingdom is being referred to in each of the following verses.

- Daniel 7:14 ____________________
- Psalm 103:19 ____________________
- John 3:3 ____________________
- Luke 1:33 ____________________
- 2 Timothy 4:1 ____________________
- John 3:5 ____________________

God's Will

What insights do the following verses give us into the will of God for our lives?

- John 6:40 ____________________
  ____
- Colossians 1:9 ____________________
  ____
  ____
- 1 Thessalonians 4:3 ____________________
  ____
  ____
- 1 Thessalonians 5:18 ____________________
  ____
- 1 Peter 4:1-2 ____________________
  ____
  ____

L E S S O N 2 0

GIVE US, FORGIVE US, DELIVER US

TEACHER'S LESSON

	Needs	*Focus*	*Time*
Give Us Our Bread			
Forgive Us Our Debts			
Deliver Us from Evil			

- ***Give Us Our Bread***
    - God delights in ______________ and repeated prayer.
    - God cares about our ____________.
    - God wants us to live ______________ at a time.
    - God wants us to pray both for __________________ and ____________.
- ***Forgive Us Our Debts***
    - Why do believers need to ask for forgiveness?

Type of Forgiveness	*Effect*	*Basis*	*Scripture*
Judicial			
Familial			

- Is our forgiveness based on whether we forgive others? ______, but forgiving others is a ________ that we have been forgiven.

- ***Deliver Us from Evil***

Type of Temptation	*Response*
Test of Endurance	
Enticement to Sin	
Assault from Satan	

- Keys to victory: ____________ and the Word of God
- Comforts in temptation
  - The example of ___________
  - The evidence of _________________
  - The encouragement of the ___________
  - The end of _________
  - The edification of the _________________

WORD POWER

- *Temptation*—an allurement to do evil; a test of your love and loyalty to God
- *Petition*—a request
- *Persistence*—unwillingness to give up
- *Intercession*—prayer to God on someone else's behalf

STUDENT'S LESSON

For the past three lessons we have been studying the various parts of the Lord's Model Prayer. One way Jesus taught His disciples about prayer was by giving them this prayer as a model. Another way He taught them important lessons about prayer was through teaching parables (stories that teach spiritual truths).

In this lesson we are going to study two parables about prayer. First, read the parables for yourself. The first one is in Luke 11:5-10, and the other is in Luke 18:1-8. Then read the following material, and be prepared to answer questions about it on the quiz.

Parable of the Persistent Friend

The Story (Luke 11:5-10)

There are three friends in this story.

The first one is the traveling friend. Instead of seeking refuge in an inn before nightfall so as to avoid the many dangers of traveling at night, he continued his journey until he reached his friend's house, even though it meant traveling until midnight.

The second friend is the host. He has been placed in a very embarrassing situation. According to the customs of his day, any time a guest arrives, he should be ready with certain signs of hospitality, which included food and drink. However, his family had eaten all the bread in the house, and fresh bread would not be baked until the next morning. He felt that the solution to his problem was to rush to the third friend's house and simply ask for the needed loaves of bread. He felt sure that his friend would understand his dilemma and would be happy to help him out of a tight situation.

The third friend is the one being asked to supply the bread. Unlike what the second friend expected, the third friend was reluctant to help. From his viewpoint, it would be better for the first friend to go hungry and wait until the morning to be fed than it would be for him to have to disturb his family in the middle of the night.

The only reason that the third friend eventually gave in to his friend's wishes was because of his persistence, his shamelessness for not being embarrassed to ask a second time (11:8). What word in 11:8 means persistence? ____________________

The third friend did not feel sorry for the first friend, neither did he honor his friendship with the second friend. He eventually gave him all the bread he needed (instead of just the three loaves that were requested originally) only because he knew that was the only way he would be able to get rid of his friend who had come at such a late hour. The second friend just would not take "no" for an answer.

The Central Teaching

The focal point of Christ's teaching in this parable was this message: persist in the ministry of intercession.

When you come into contact with someone who has a need that you cannot meet, you are to become his intercessor. True intercession is not just asking for something one time and then forgetting it; on the contrary, true intercession involves persistent pleading.

What is Christ's analogy in this parable? Is He comparing the Father to the reluctant friend (the third friend) in the story and saying that we must beg Him and persuade Him to bless us? Of course not. God's ears are open to the prayers of His people, and He desires to bless them (Matt. 6:30-33; 1 Pet. 3:12).

Here Christ is teaching us the lesson of persistent intercession by contrasting the Father with the reluctant friend. His reasoning is: if even an unwilling friend responds to such persistence, how much more will your heavenly Father respond to the persistence of an intercessor! His challenge to us is: "Keep on asking, and it will be given to you; keep on seeking, and you will find; keep on knocking, and the door will be opened to you."

Parable of the Persistent Widow

The Story (Luke 18:1-8)

This story deals with a widow who was being wronged by an adversary. She was innocent and had a good case against him, so she decided to take her case before the judge in her city. Jesus described him as one who was not a God-fearer and who wasn't respectful toward people. At first the judge refused to remedy the widow's situation. However, this did not discourage her, and she continued to present her case again and again because she knew she was right. Finally she received justice from the unjust judge—simply because he no longer wanted to be bothered by this persistent widow.

The Central Teaching

Christ's main point was: persist in beseeching God to do what is right when you are being wronged. This parable is set within the context of the last days when God's people will be undergoing intense and unjust persecution. Our Lord used the same method of contrast that He used in the parable of the persistent friend. His reasoning was: if an unjust judge can be moved to administer justice by the persistence of somene who is pleading for a just cause, how much more will our heavenly Father who is both merciful and just avenge the cause of His chosen ones who cry to Him day and night concerning their righteous causes!

Christ is encouraging us to continue praying when we are being oppressed and not to give up. Do you know what it is to desire so much for God to work that you continue day by day to plead with Him to do what is right? Persistence in prayer is not a sign that you doubt God. Rather it is a sign of faith in God's power to make the wrong right. The doubting person only asks once and then forgets about it; the believing person keeps on asking until he sees God answer.

- Read the stories of these two parables once again. List three lessons that you see in these parables that will help you in your prayer life.

  ____
  ____
  ____
  ____
  ____
  ____
  ____
  ____
  ____

COMMUNICATION

WITNESSING

Another function of life is communication. From the smiles and quiet babbling of the infant to the well-spoken thoughts of the adult, man communicates the message of the "new birth" wherever he goes and whatever he does. It is conveyed by his words, actions, and attitudes to a lost world (Rom. 10:14-17). Man communicates his life experiences to others. The Christian communicates his experience of eternal life to others. First John 1:3 tells us that our words ought to be declaring the things we have seen and heard in the Word.

THE NECESSITY OF WITNESSING

TEACHER'S LESSON

- ***The ____________________ Fuels It***
- ***The ________________ of Man Demands It***
    - Completely ____________ (Isa. 1:5-6)
        - Mind (Eph. 2:3)
        - Heart (Jer. 17:9)
    - __________________ (Rom. 3:10-12)
- ***The ________________________ Requires It***
    - ____________(Acts 4:12)
    - _______________
        - A __________ of the Holy Spirit (1 Cor. 6:19)
        - An ________________________ (representative) for Christ (2 Cor. 5:20)
        - ________________ over Sin (1 John 5:4)
- ***The ________________________ Constrains It***
    - Our love __________________ ("He loved us"—1 John 4:10)
    - Christ's love ___________("love one another"—1 John 4:11)
- ***The ____________________________ Compels It***

- Hell's...
  - ____________________(Matt. 8:12)
  - ___________(Matt. 3:12; Jude 23)
  - _________ (Matt. 13:50)
  - ________________________________ (Rev. 9:2)
  - ______________________ (Luke 16:23-24)
  - _____________ (Matt. 8:12; 13:50)
  - _____________ (Luke 16:24)
  - ___________________________(2 Thess. 1:9)

WORD POWER

- ***Witnessing***—giving testimony to the gospel of Jesus Christ by sharing what Christ has done on the cross and in one's life

STUDENT'S LESSON

- This lesson begins the fourth section of our study on the Christian life. What are the first three functions of life we have studied? _________________________________

  ____

  ____

This section deals with that important task of communicating to others what Christ has done for us and what He can do for them. The work of communicating the faith is often spoken of as witnessing or soul-winning.

What is Communication?

The word "communicate" means to convey knowledge or information about something. Communication, then, is simply telling others what you saw, heard, or felt.

- John 1:32-34 is a perfect example of communication in its simplest form. What is it? ____

- What does a Christian have that should be made known or made common to all (1 Thess. 2:4, 8, 9)? ______________________________

- What do the following verses say about the message of salvation?

  - Ephesians 1:7 ______________________________
    ____
    ____

  - Romans 5:1 ______________________________
    ____
    ____

  - Hebrews 9:12 ______________________________
    ____

  - 1 Peter 1:4 ______________________________
    ____
    ____

  - Acts 10:43 ______________________________
    ____
    ____

Why Should a Christian Communicate This Message?

It Glorifies the Godhead

The first and greatest reason believers should witness is because it brings glory and honor to the Lord. Sadly, we are often challenged to witness because of our compassion for the lost condition of our friends! As we shall see, this is a reason we should witness, but it is not the greatest reason we should tell others of the gospel. Communicating the gospel should be first and foremost the natural result of our being so full of God and so zealous for His glory that we want the whole world to hear!

Note the following verses of Scripture relating to this:

- Psalm 51:12-13—When I have the joy of my salvation, I will automatically tell others about Him.
- Romans 1:1, 3, 5—Paul was set apart for the gospel, which concerns God's Son through whom he was given grace to preach the gospel to all Gentiles for His name's sake (that is, for His glory). Paul here reveals that the reason he was called to preach the gospel was for the sake of God's glorious name. Seeing men saved is seeing God's name glorified!
- Acts 15:14—God's plan for our age is that He would call out of all nations a people for His name! It is His name that is most important. We witness because we want men to know about His name.
- Romans 1:16-17—Paul was not ashamed of the gospel because it revealed two things about God: (1) His power and (2) His righteousness.

The Three "Onlys"

Another reason believers should witness is because of the three "onlys."

- There is only one name given whereby we must be s________ (Acts 4:12).
- There is only one way to believe on Him by h____________ about Him first (Rom. 10:14).
- There is only one escape from j______________ (Heb. 2:3; 10:26-27).

The Power of the Message

He should communicate because of the power of the message. In your own words, explain what this message can do.

- The message of Christ has the power to ______________________________ ____ (Rom. 1:16).
- The message of Christ has the power to ______________________________ (John 6:63).

- The message of Christ has the power to ______________________________
____ (1 Pet. 1:23).

- The message of Christ has the power to ______________________________ (2 Cor. 5:19).

Christ's Command

He should communicate because Christ commanded it (Matt. 28:19; Acts 1:8). While God does command us to witness, this should not be the main reason we witness! If I witness only because I am commanded to, my witnessing will be little more than going through the motions. It will be a mere duty witout passion.

Man's Responsibility

He should communicate because of man's responsibility.

- In 2 Corinthians 5:10-11, why did Paul say he persuaded men?

  ____

  ____

- Note the word "therefore." This is a word that points backward to what has previously been stated. Thus, to what does the terror (or fear) of the Lord refer? ______________________________________

- Who must appear at the judgment seat of Christ? ____________________

Note Paul's reference to the fact that we will receive the things done whether good or bad. Then he immediately says, "Therefore . . . we persuade other people." Paul felt responsible to God for witnessing; he felt he would have to account to God for his faithfulness to witness.

Remember, God goes nowhere that we don't take Him. God speaks only through men! He uses our mouths, our tongues, our words. He has chosen to work only through mankind. How can they hear without a preacher? We are responsible to God for the way we handle this ministry.

- According to 1 Thessalonians 2:4 and 9, did Paul just take it upon himself to witness? ☐ Yes ☐ No

- What does Paul mean by saying that God had entrusted them with the gospel? ______________________________

- To whom was Paul responsible for the way he handled the gospel? ______

- What words express this? ______________________________
____

- How did Paul carry out this responsibility (verse 9)? ______________
____

- What did Paul want to avoid with those to whom he was preaching the gospel? ______________________________
____

Refusing to preach would make him continue to be indebted to them (Rom. 1:14).

Man's Spiritual Condition

The Nature of Man's Spiritual Condition

Finally, we need to witness due to man's spiritual condition. Man's physical and material condition is no indication of his spiritual condition.

Look up the following and state what each says about man's spiritual condition.

- Isaiah 64:6 ______________________________
____

- Job 25:6 ______________________________

- Jeremiah 17:9 ______________________________
____

- 2 Corinthians 4:3-4 ______________________________

  (It is interesting to note the reason Satan blinds men to the gospel—so that God will not get the glory! Satan's goal is not so much to see men go to hell as it is to keep God from being glorified by men seeing His majesty in salvation.)

- Ephesians 2:1 ______________________________

- Ephesians 2:12 ______________________________

____

____

- Ephesians 4:18 ______________________________

____

____

- Ephesians 4:19 ______________________________

____

____

- Romans 3:10 ______________________________
- Romans 3:11 ______________________________

____

- Romans 3:12 ______________________________

____

____

- Romans 3:13-18 ______________________________

____

____

____

____

____

- John 3:18 ______________________________

____

- How many people are in this condition according to Romans 3:23?

______

- According to 1 John 5:19? ______________________________

The Results of Man's Spiritual Condition

Note the results of man's spiritual condition. Look up the following verses and state in your own words how man's spiritual bankruptcy affects his life.

- Matthew 12:33-37 ______________________________

  ____

- Matthew 15:18-20 ______________________________

  ____

  ____

  ____

  ____

- Ephesians 4:19 ______________________________

  ____

  ____

  ____

- James 4:1 ______________________________

  ____

  ____

- Read Romans 1:28-32. Are the twenty-three things listed in this passage the root or the fruit of man's problems? ____________________

- What does verse 28 say about this? ____________________

  ____

  ____

  ____

- Put these verses together and answer the following questions.
  - Is man's basic problem inward or outward? ____________________
  - Is man's basic problem hereditary or environmental?

    ____

- Sociologists state that man's problems are the result of poor housing, ignorance, or poor income. Thus, the answer to man's problems, they say, is to improve his housing, educate him, and give him a guaranteed minimum wage. Is this true? ☐ Yes ☐ No
- Why or why not? ______________________________________

____

____

HOW TO WITNESS

TEACHER'S LESSON

- ***Five Stages to Witnessing***
  - Summary
    - ____________________
    - ____________________
    - ____________________
    - ____________________
    - ____________________
  - Definition
    - Witnessing is sharing with others ____________________ and ____________________.
  - Personal ____________
    - How Jesus witnessed to the Samaritan woman (John 4)
      - In a ________ place (4:6)
      - To an ____________ (4:8-9)
      - With casual ____________ (4:9-10)
      - In spite of His____________(4:6)
  - Spiritual ____________
    - He made her aware of a ____________________
      - By ________ something unusual (speaking to a ____________ ____________)
      - By ________ something unusual (about ____________water that will keep you from ever being ____________ again)

- He used ______________________ elements (like __________)
- He led to the ______________________
    - A ________ of God (4:10)
    - ____________________ life (4:14)
    - __________________ (4:22)
    - ____________ (4:24)
    - The ____________ of God (4:24)
    - The ______________ (4:26)

WORD POWER

- *Samaritans*—a half-Jewish ethinic group who lived just north of Jerusalem and were despised by most Jews in Christ's day
- *Conviction*—a work of the Holy Spirit by which a person is gripped by the power of the gospel and pricked in his heart over his sin

STUDENT'S LESSON

This is the first of a four-part study on the stages to winning a person to Christ. There are five stages to bringing a person to a saving knowledge of Jesus Christ: (1) making personal contact; (2) arousing spiritual curiosity; (3) communicating what Christ means to you; (4) experiencing the conviction of the Holy Spirit; and (5) clinching the decision. You can remember these points by using the letter C: contact, curiosity, communication, conviction, and clinching.

This first study will deal with the definition of witnessing and the first two steps.

What Is Witnessing?

Note examples of witnessing in Acts 4:33; 5:42, and 9:20-22.

- Concerning what did the apostles witness in Acts 4:33? ________________

  ____
- What was the theme of the preaching in Acts 5:42? ________________

- What was the subject of the communication in Acts 9:20-22? ______________

  ____

- Did the disciples give a four-point outline on "How to Get Saved" in these passages? ☐ Yes ☐ No

- We often think that witnessing means telling people that (1) they are sinners; (2) they must die for their sin; (3) Christ died for them; and (4) if they will trust Christ, they will be saved. All four of these points are important, but can a person be a witness without going through all these points? ☐ Yes ☐ No

Witnessing is simply sharing with others who Christ is and what He means to you.

What Are the First Two Stages in Witnessing?

The five stages in witnessing that we've begun to study in this lesson all come from Christ's conversation with the Samaritan woman recorded in John 4. They are not the only way to present the gospel. They are just one way. Since every situation and individual is unique, you will need to read your environment and adapt in order to communicate effectively who Christ is and what He has done for you. You cannot put evangelism into a strait jacket. Jesus Christ, whom we're studying in John 4, also gave the good news in many different ways during His earthly life. Even the apostle Paul had to ask for prayer that he would have wisdom to know how to present the gospel as he should (Col. 4:3-4, see also Eph. 6:18-20). The gospel never changes, but no two situations are the same. Think of these five steps as some basic building blocks, that you can rearrange and use (along with other building blocks from other Bible passages) to build the gospel to best communicate to your unbelieving friend. Let's look at the first stage Christ models in John 4.

Make the Personal Contact

- Personal contact is important. Read John 4:6-18. Of what ethnic group (race) was the woman at the well? ______________________

This was a group of people who were a mixture of Jew and Gentile, and therefore, despised by both groups. Most Jews would not even travel through Samaria but traveled miles out of the way to bypass it.

- What does the last sentence of verse 9 tell us about the relationship between Jews and Samaritans? ______________________________
____
- Did the woman expect Jesus to shun her? ☐ Yes ☐ No
- Did He shun her? ☐ Yes ☐ No

We often fail to witness because many unsaved people don't appeal to us or make us feel uncomfortable. However we cannot witness to a person that we do not take the time to get to know.

- Read 2 Corinthians 6:14. Should a Christian make close friendships with an unsaved person? ☐ Yes ☐ No
- Why or why not? ______________________________
____
____
____
- Does this mean we should totally avoid unsaved people? ☐ Yes ☐ No
- Why or why not? ______________________________
____
____
____

Arouse Spiritual Curiosity

First, a person must win the friendship of the unsaved. Next, he begins to share Christ with them in such a way as to tactfully arouse their interest in spiritual things. But how is this done? Note John 4 again.

- In what way did Christ arouse this woman's interest in spiritual things?
____
____
- What did He offer her that was especially interesting and unusual?
____

Christ turned a conversation about an ordinary thing (water) into a discussion of what Christ had to offer (living water). This offer made the woman aware of her own need. This is the purpose of sharing with others what Christ means to us; it makes people aware of their own need.

- In what way did the woman express her need? ____________________
  ____
- Did the woman ask any questions? ☐ Yes ☐ No
- How many (after verse 10)? ______
- What were they? ______________________________________
  ____
  ____

The key to witnessing is arousing a person's interest in his own needs to the point that he is asking the questions.

What Can We Conclude?

- What is witnessing? ______________________________________
  ____
  ____
- Name the first two stages in witnessing. ________________________
  ____
- What is the purpose for sharing with others what Christ means to us?
  ____
  ____
- What is a key to encouraging the unbeliever to start asking questions?
  ____
  ____

THE POWER OF THE GOSPEL

TEACHER'S LESSON

- ***What Is the Most Powerful Force on Earth?***
  - Money?
  - Nuclear power?
  - Influence?
  - No! The ____________!
- ***Power to ________***
  - Declared (Rom. 1:16)
    - It is power from _____
    - It is power resulting in ________________
    - It is power to every person who ______________
  - Illustrated (in Acts)
    - _________ saved (2:37-41)
    - More saved: total of _________ men (4:4)
- ***Power to ________***
  - Declared (1 Pet. 1:5, Heb. 13:5, and John 6:37)
  - Illustrated—no one can _________ us out of the _______________ hand (John 10:28-30)
- ***Power to ____________________***

- Declared (2 Cor. 5:17)
- Illustrated
  - ________________________ transformed (Acts 9:1, 20-21)
  - ____________________________ transformed (Luke 8:2)
  - ___________________________ transformed (Mark 5:1-20)

WORD POWER

- *Transformation*—a change into something different
- *Keep*—to protect and preserve

STUDENT'S LESSON

- List the five stages in witnessing. ____________________________

  ____

  ____

  ____

This lesson deals with the third and fourth stages in effective witnessing: communicating (sharing) Christ and conviction of the Spirit.

Communicating Christ

After personal contact is established, the witness begins to arouse the spiritual interest by constantly relating things to the Lord.

At this point the unsaved teen becomes aware of his needs and soon may begin asking questions. Whether or not the questions come, the saved teen continues to share Christ and what He means personally to his life.

Read the following verses and state what they teach about sharing Christ.

- Acts 4:12 ____________________________________

  ____

  ____

  ____

- Romans 10:17 ____

  ____

- 1 Corinthians 2:1-2 ______________________________________

  ____

  ____

- How does one share Christ? ________________________________

  ____

  ____

Now let's personalize these truths.

- State several things that Christ has done for you that you can share with the unsaved. (Be specific. Don't just write things like, "He saved me," or "He gave me new life.") ____

  ____

  ____

  ____

- Do you ever share this testimony with the unsaved? ☐ Yes ☐ No
- When was the last time you shared with an unsaved person what Christ means to you? ____
- What happened when you shared this? ___________________________

  ____

Note Paul's preaching in each of the following texts and state the theme or major subject of each message and the results.

- The theme of Acts 13:14-43 is: ____________________________

  ____

- The results are: ____

  ____

  ____

- In Acts 16:25-36, what did Paul and Silas do (one of the five stages in witnessing)? ____

- Was the second step (second stage of witnessing) taken? ☐ Yes ☐ No
- How do you know? ____

  ____
- Did they communicate Christ? ☐ Yes ☐ No
- How? ____

  ____

  ____
- The theme of Acts 17:19-34 is: ____

  ____
- The results are: ____

  ____

  ____
- The theme of Acts 22:1-23 is: ____

  ____
- The results are: ____

  ____

  ____

Conviction of the Holy Spirit

- According to John 16:7-11, who is the Comforter? ____________________

  ____
- What does He do (16:8)? ____

  ____

  ____
- The Holy Spirit alone can convict a soul of its need of Christ. We often say, "Witnessing is hard. I can't do it." Is it hard to talk about anything or anyone you love? ☐ Yes ☐ No

- Actually, what is our part in soul-winning? ______________________________

____

____

____

- What is the Spirit's part? ______________________________

- Who does the work in soul-winning? ______________________________

- What is the power in witnessing (Rom. 1:16)? ______________________________

____

Sin Inc.
Any one who sins
Death
ROMANS 3:23
Anytime
$ 1 Death
PENALTY
U.R. Life

SIN AND ITS PENALTY

TEACHER'S LESSON

- ***Clinching the Decision***
  - Show him he is a ____________
    - By the transformation in your ________
    - By the testimony of ____________________
      - God's ________________ (He is the perfect ______________)
      - God's ____________
        - Based on His _______________ (He Is ______ - 1 Pet. 1:16)
        - Expressed in His ______________________

          Purposes of God's law (Rom. 3:19-20; Gal. 3:19, 24):

          - Stops ___________
          - Legally _______________
          - Shows what ________ is
          - Points to need of ____________
        - Illustrated in His _______ (Matt. 19:16-26)

          Money was more important to the young man than obedience to God.
    - With a practical approach (e.g., Philip and Ethiopian eunuch)
      - Make the verses _________ and ___________
      - Make the verses ______________
      - Make sure the person ____________________
  - Show him the _______________ for his ______
    - ________________ death (Rom. 6:23)

- ____________ death (Rev. 20:14-15)

- Show him his personal accountability
  - Everyone shall give an ______________ of himself to God (Rom. 14:12)
  - We shall give ______________ to the One who is ready to __________ everyone (1 Pet. 4:5)
  - It is a ______________ thing to fall into the hands of the living God (Heb. 10:31)
  - God will ____________the dead from a _______________________ ______________ (Rev. 20:11-15)

WORD POWER

- *Demand*—a requirement
- *Penalty*—a consequence for wrong-doing
- *Accountability*—responsiblity for one's actions monitored by another person

STUDENT'S LESSON

- List the five stages in witnessing. ______________________________
____
____
____

This lesson begins a two-part study of the fifth stage—clinching the decision. Often a teen will say, "I've laid the groundwork, shared Christ with the unsaved, and lived a consistent life. Now the person says he wants to be saved! What do I do? What do I say?"

Basically there are four facts the unsaved teen needs to know in order to be saved: (1) he is a sinner, (2) he must pay for his sin, (3) Christ paid the price for him, and (4) he needs to repent, trust Christ, and accept the payment.

In the teacher's lesson we studied the first two facts.

Show Him He Is a Sinner

Naturally, the teen may have already seen this through previous experiences. He may, through your life and constant sharing of Christ, have already seen his need and for this reason may want to have what you have. In either case, he needs to have impressed upon him the need for his salvation.

The following verses may be used to establish the teen's sinfulness: Ecclesiastes 7:20, Isaiah 53:6, Jeremiah 17:9, Romans 3:10-12, 23, and Galatians 3:22.

How many of these verses should you use? The answer depends on how quickly he sees his need of Christ. Some readily admit their sin, while others need several months of thinking to come under conviction. Usually when a person is ready to be saved, only one or two verses are needed.

There are three rules to follow as you use these verses.

Make the Verses Clear and Simple

Explain what they mean. For example, explain the following verses in Romans 3 as if you were dealing with a teen named Ben Lost. (Also, be sure to explain such words as "righteous," "unprofitable," and "sin.")

- Verse 10 ____

  ____

  ____

- Verse 11 ____

  ____

  ____

- Verse 12 ____

  ____

  ____

- Verse 23 ____

  ____

  ____

Make Them Personal

- Substitute the teen's name for such words as "all" and "whoever." How could you read Isaiah 53:6 to Ben Lost? ________________________________

  ____

  ____

Make Sure the Person Understands What the Verses Say

After explaining the meaning of the verses and making them as personal as you know how, ask the teen to tell you what the verses said. Then ask: "Ben, do you believe you are a sinner?" (Yes.) "Why do you believe this?" (God's Word says I am.)

Show Him the Penalty for Sin

At this point, Ben Lost may be thinking: "So I'm a sinner. So what? Everyone else is a sinner too. What's so bad about that?"

It may be good even to state the above thought. If you can understand and say what he is thinking, you are a long way toward reaching him. After stating the question, show him what's so bad about being a sinner: death (Rom. 6:23; Eze. 18:4), hell, and the lake of fire (Luke 16:23; Rev. 20:15)—in other words, offending a holy God and having to suffer the punishment for sin.

Again, make it clear and personal. Be sure he understands and admits what it means before going any further.

It may be good to point out that since all men are sinners, all men must die, both saved sinners and unsaved sinners. But there the similarity ends, for at death the saved sinner goes to heaven, and the unsaved sinner goes to hell.

TRUSTING CHRIST AS SAVIOR

TEACHER'S LESSON

Clinching the Decision: 4 Facts the Sinner Must Know

- ***Man Is a ___________***
- ***Man Must Pay a ________________ for His ______***
- ***Christ _________ for Man's ______***
    - False theories of Christ's death
        - _______________ theory: his death could be no _______________ because it was ____________________ in the Old Testament
            - _____________ (Zech. 11:13)
            - ____________ (Isa. 53:7)
            - Bruises and __________ (Isa. 53:5)
            - ____________ hands and feet (Ps. 22:16)
            - Crucifixion with ____________ (Isa. 53:12)
        - ___________ theory: Christ ____________ the cross, but ____________ look forward to death (Luke 22:42)
        - The moral influence or example theory: Christ was more than our example; He was our _______________

- The true meaning of Christ's death
  - Christ died . . .
    - For man's ______: for our __________________________(Acts 13:38) and our _______________ (1 Pet. 2:24)
    - As man's substitute, Christ was made ________ for us, and we are made ____________________ in Him (2 Cor. 5:21).
    - That man might _________ (Eph. 2:1, 5)

- ***Man Must ____________ Christ for _____________________***
  - Man's ________________________
    - He will not ___________________________ (John 5:40)
    - He has been _______________ by Satan (2 Cor. 4:3-4)
    - He has no _______________________________ (Eph. 4:18)
  - God's __________
    - The Spirit _______________________ of __________, ______________________________, and ___________________ (John 16:7-11)
    - The Spirit ___________________ "whosoever will" to _____________________________________ (Rev. 22:17)
  - Trusting Christ
    - Admit. . .
      - You are a _____________ (Rom. 3:10-12, 23; 5:12; Gal. 3:22)
      - You must _______ for your sin (Ezek. 18:4; Rom. 6:23; James 1:15)
      - You must _______________________________ for your sin (Luke 16:22-23; Rev. 20:15)
    - Believe. . .
      - God ___________ you (Jer. 31:3; John 3:16)
      - Christ _________ for you (Rom. 5:6, 8; 1 Pet. 2:24)
      - If you ___________ Him, He will save you (John 3:16; Acts 16:31; Rom. 4:5)

- Commit . . .
  - Yourself to Christ as ________ , ________, and ___________ (John 20:28-29; Rom. 10:9)
  - Your ________ to Christ for ____________________on the basis of what He did for you in his __________, ___________, and resurrection (Rom. 10:9; 1 Cor. 15:1-4)

WORD POWER

- *Martyr*—someone who gives their life for a cause
- *Substitute*—someone who stands in the place of another

STUDENT'S LESSON

- What are the first two facts you show a person when you are clinching a decision? ____

  ____

This lesson deals with the third and fourth facts a person must believe for salvation—Christ died on the cross as payment for his sin, and he must trust Christ for salvation.

Christ Died for Man's Sin

- Choose four good verses from the following that state that Christ died for man's sin: John 3:16; Acts 16:31; Romans 5:8; Ephesians 2:8; Hebrews 9:28; 1 Peter 2:24 and 3:18. ____

  ____

- If the penalty for man's sin has already been paid by Christ, what can we logically conclude is left for man to do? ______________________________

  ____

- The key word to describe Christ's death is "substitution." In what way was Christ's death substitutionary? ______________________________

  ____

- Think of a good illustration for substitution that you might use at this point in witnessing. Write the general idea for the illustration.

  ____

  ____

  ____

What Must a Person Do to Be Saved?

Verses About Salvation

Read each verse below and state what it says a person must do to be saved.

- John 1:12 ____

  ____

- Acts 16:31 ____

  ____

- Romans 10:9 ____

  ____

  ____

  ____

- What does it mean to "trust" or "receive" Christ? ____________________

  ____

  ____

  ____

The Logic of Salvation

- Note the logic: you owe a debt. What debt does the sinner owe?

  ____

- Christ paid it for you. How? ____

- If your debt has been paid, you only have two alternatives: ____________ or ____________ the payment.

- Does this call for any special work on the part of the person in debt?

  ☐ Yes ☐ No

For example, suppose a man owed $10 to a store, and someone paid the debt for him. What would be left for the man to do? He would only have to accept the payment. But suppose he said: "Oh, thank you for paying my debt! I'll go jump in the lake right now, and then I'll join the Moose Lodge!" You would think he was crazy! Yet, some people think that since Christ paid our sin debt, they must be baptized and join the church for it to do them any good.

- What does Ephesians 2:8-9 say about this type of logic? ______________

  ____

  ____

  ____

How Do We Get a Sinner to Trust Christ?

We don't. The Holy Spirit does. There are many methods being recommended today. Some even tell you how to phrase your statements so the person will almost have to say "yes." Some show you how to put your hand on a person's shoulder and put pressure on them to bow and trust Christ. Don't ever forget that your job is to present the person with his sinfulness, his sin's consequences, and Christ's payment for his sin. Then simply ask him if he would like to trust Christ. Depend on the Holy Spirit to get the job done.

There are various ways of presenting the sinner with his need. The Romans Road (Rom. 3:23; 6:23; 5:8; 10:9) is used by some, while others use various verses. Study the ABC plan presented in the teacher's lesson.

At this point ask these questions: Will you right this moment trust Christ as your Lord and Savior? (If the person answers "yes," then proceed.) Did you just now give yourself to Christ to do anything with you He desires from now on? (This is confessing Him as Lord.) Did you just now trust Christ and what He did on the cross to save you forever? (This is believing in your heart that God raised Him from the dead.)

When the sinner places his faith in all of the above, God says he is saved at that moment and forever (2 Tim. 1:12; 1 John 5:12-13).

- How should these truths affect the way you witness? ______________________

  ____

  ____

  ____

What Do You Do Immediately After a Person Is Saved?

Now that the person has said, "Yes, I am trusting Christ right now," discuss the following truths to help him understand what he has done.

Ask Him If He Is Saved

If he answers, "I don't know," share with him Christ's promise in John 5:24. Remind him that salvation is not based on how well he believed or prayed. Instead, it is based on the promise of the true and faithful God. Remember, it is not your responsibility to produce assurance because true assurance comes only through the work of the Holy Spirit bringing conviction of the truth of God's Word.

However, if it seems that he genuinely doesn't understand something, you can ask if there is anything you looked at in the Bible that he didn't understand or that wasn't clear. If he says yes and tells you what he didn't understand, then you can go over those passages with him again.

Point Him to the Power for the Christian Life

When we are saved, we are freed from the bondage of the sins and desires of our old man. A new believer needs to know that he is now in Christ and has the power of Christ dwelling in him in the person of the Holy Spirit. As he abides in Christ he will begin to produce the fruit of the Spirit. This will bring great assurance of his salvation.

Encourage the new believer to spend time reading the Bible. There he will learn more of his new Lord and more about how he can serve this gracious Master. A true believer will also find assurance from time spent in communion in the Word.

Take a moment also to teach him that he can now pray to God any time he wants. He will especially want to pray for power to love and obey God and His Word. The new believer will need to be taught to pray for forgiveness whenever he sins. Without knowing this, he will be easy prey for attacks of doubt the first time he fails his new Lord.

Encourage Him to Get Involved with Believers at a Good Church

The Body of Christ is one of the tools God uses to help give assurance to believers. Christ uses His Body to encourage and help build up believers in their newly-found faith (Eph. 4:18). As the new believer grows with other believers around him (seeing him and helping him), he will be encouraged by the work of grace that God has begun in his heart.

FOLLOWING UP

TEACHER'S LESSON

- ***The Importance of Follow-Up***
  - It is commanded
    - The ______________________________ (Matt. 28:19-20)
      - __________________ and ________________ are inseparable
      - Discipleship includes instruction on obedience
    - ___________ teaching (2 Tim. 2:2)
      - Definite ____________
      - Definite _________________
  - It shows ______________
- ***The Methods of Follow-Up***
  - One-to-one
    - Explain _________________
    - Assist in ___________________________________
    - Assist in ___________
    - Invite him to your _____________
  - In the youth group
  - In church
- ***The Goals of Follow-Up***
  - Conformity to Christ—spiritual _________________ (Rom. 8:29)
  - Participation in minstry—spiritual ____________ (Eph. 4:11-13)
  - Multiplication of disciples—spiritual ______________________ (2 Tim. 3:16-17)

WORD POWER

- *Convert*—a new Christian
- *Disciple*—a person who learns from and imitates Jesus Christ
- *Discipleship*—process of growing as a Christian

STUDENT'S LESSON

- List the five stages in witnessing. ____________________

  ____

  ____

  ____

- List the four facts a person must be shown in clinching the decision.

  ____

  ____

  ____

  ____

- What are the ABC's of salvation? ____________________

  ____

  ____

  ____

- After the person has trusted Christ, he needs to be strengthened. What does John 3:3 say a person has to do to go to heaven? ____________________
- What do you think it means to be "born again"? ____________________

  ____

Thus a new Christian is like a newborn baby. He is weak and unable to walk, talk, or think properly. He must be strengthened, fed, exercised, and nurtured. The following five things should be given to the newborn Christian to strengthen him. Make sure he understands that these things will not keep him saved or save him. These only help make him a stronger Christian.

He Should See and Savor Jesus Christ Every Day

- Read Hebews 12:1-2. As a new convert runs the Christian race, on whom should he keep his focus? ____

____

____

- Read 2 Corinthians 3:16-18. What is it that we are helped by the Holy Spirit to see, now that we're Christians? ____

____

- According to this passage, what is the result of seeing the glory of God with our spiritual eyes? ____

____

____

____

- So, what is it that helps us grow spiritually? ____

____

____

____

- Read Hebrews 13:9 and Titus 2:12-13. What is it that gives spiritual strength and teaches us to deny our flesh? ____

- What should you help encourage a new convert to look to and rely on everyday for strength? ____

____

____

____

He Should Read God's Word Every Day

The Bible is the Christian's food. Just as we all (especially a baby) need food for strength, the new Christian must eat spiritual food daily if he is to be a strong Christian. How do the following verses describe the Bible as it relates to food?

- Psalm 119:103 ____________________

____

- Isaiah 55:10-11 ____________________

____

- Hebrews 5:12-14 ____________________

____

- 1 Peter 2:2 ____________________

____

The best book to have a newborn Christian begin reading is the Gospel of John. This Gospel magnifies the deity of Christ and further explains His simple plan of salvation.

How much should a new Christian read each day? Only as much as he can digest. By that we mean only as much as he can understand and think about that day. Many Christians try to read too much each day, and about three fourths of what they read is lost either because they don't understand it, they lose their concentration, or they forget what they read. A small portion, well-digested, is far better than a large portion quickly forgotten.

He Should Pray Every Day

As we've already learned, prayer is essentially communion with God. Prayer is not just the means of getting what we want from God's hands. As you go through this section on the importance of prayer for a new convert, don't forget to remind the new believer that prayer is talking to your Father. It's the overflow and outworking of your relationship with God, not some awful task or duty that you must check off your list every day. When you pray, you are talking to a Person—your loving, heavenly Father.

Ephesians 6:18 underlines the importance of prayer. Note the following from this forceful verse.

- When should we pray? ____________________
- In whom should we pray? ____________________
- For whom should we pray? ____________________
- With what quality should we pray? ____________________

____

The word "watching" literally means being sleepless. Paul realized the natural laziness of man, especially when it comes to prayer. How seldom we pray things through. We tend to get right to the point of a great blessing in prayer and then get drowsy or lose our concentration and quit.

But why should a Christian give so much time and attention to prayer? Notice the following five reasons.

There Is a Devil

- Ephesians 6:12 tells us that we have enemies against whom we must wrestle. Who are these enemies? ______________________________________

  ____

  ____

- The verses that follow show how to have victory over these enemies. Name the things we should wear to bring us this victory.

  ____

  ____

  ____

Paul then concludes with the verse we already read (verse 18). If we do not have a meaningful prayer life, we will spend our days totally defeated by Satan.

Prayer Is God's Way for Us to Obtain Things

- According to James 4:2, why do men lack things in their lives?

  ____

These words contain the reason for the spiritual poverty and powerlessness of most Christians—neglect of prayer.

Prayer Is an Important Part of Christ's Present Ministry

- According to Hebrews 7:25, what is Christ presently doing?

  ____

Here we see why Christ lives in heaven. He is speaking to God on our behalf when we pray.

- According to Romans 8:34, why is Christ in heaven? ____________________

  ____

Nothing should so impress us with a sense of the importance of praying at all times as the thought that this is the principal occupation of our risen Lord at the present time.

Prayer Is the Means of Obtaining Mercy and Grace

- What does Hebrews 4:16 say about this? ____________________

  ____

  ____

  ____

Prayer Is the Means of Freedom from Worry and Care

- What does Philippians 4:6-7 promise the praying Christian?

  ____

  ____

  ____

He Should Tell Others About His New Birth

- What did the Samaritan woman do immediately after trusting Christ (John 4:25-30)? ____________________

  ____

  ____

This is the natural desire of every newborn Christian. Nothing will so strengthen him as telling his loved ones and friends what Christ has done for him.

He Should Join a Gospel-believing Church, Be Baptized, and Attend the Church Faithfully

- What did Peter command the new Christians to do in Acts 10:44-48?

  ____

  ____

- What had they done, and what had already happened to them before they were baptized? ____

____

Thus, baptism couldn't save them; they had to be saved before they got baptized.

- What does the Bible say about church attendance in Hebrews 10:25?

____

____

The new Christian needs the fellowship of older Christians, besides the need for learning the Word from Christians who have studied the Scriptures through the years.

What are five things you should encourage a new Christian to do?

1. ____
____
2. ____
____
3. ____
____
4. ____
____
5. ____
____

HANDLING EXCUSES

TEACHER'S LESSON

Christ's Commentary on Excuses (Luke 14:15-24)

- ***Dealing with Other Excuses***
  - "I'll wait until later."
    - ______ is the time (2 Cor. 6:2)
    - Don't wait for __________________(Prov. 27:1)
  - "I have sinned too much."
    - God saved the ____ (1 Tim. 1:15)
    - God shows His __________to sinners (Rom. 5:8)
    - God never ___________________ those who turn to Him (John 6:37)
  - "My friends aren't Christians, and I can't do without them."
    - _____________ of the world are enemies of God (James 4:4)
    - The Lord will become your ___________ (John 15:15)
- ***Themes of Excuses***
  - __________________ isn't worth it
    - "The world means too much to me"
      - The way of the world is _______ (Prov. 13:15)
      - God's way is a _______________ way (Prov. 3:17)
    - "I'm going to risk _______________ without ___________"

- "I don't want a __________ for my life"
    - Your way only ______________________ (Prov. 14:12)
    - One day you will __________________________ Him (Phil. 2:10-11)
- God is untruthful
  - "I'm _____________ to be a Christian"
    - ____________________ comes from the Lord
    - Our efforts cannot ____________ God
  - "I won't be punished ______________"
  - "I can't be sure if Christ will ______________ me"

- ***Deal with Excuses, but Don't Offend Unnecessarily***
  - Be _____________________ aware of the sinner's condition
  - Never ___________ with the sinner
  - Grant the sinner _____________________ every time you get a chance
  - Let the sinner know that you _______________________ him
  - The attitude that wins is _________

WORD POWER

- *Hypocrite*—someone who pretends to be one thing but is really another

STUDENT'S LESSON

Excuses come only from those who are not yet under strong conviction of sin. They may be convicted to a point, but once a man comes under the heavy hand of the Holy Spirit, his excuses begin to buckle and fall. It is our responsibility to meet these excuses with Scripture so that the Holy Spirit might begin to work and remove these excuses from the sinner's mind.

Does that mean that we should not argue with the sinner? That's right. Instead, we should let the Word of God and the Holy Spirit do the work. When we hear excuses, we should not try to argue about how ridiculous the excuses are, but we should busy ourselves placing the "dynamite sticks" of Scripture in the sinner's mind for the Spirit to use in exploding the excuses.

So let's get started. We will give you the dynamite verses and explain them for each of the excuses below.

"There Are Too Many Hypocrites in the Church"

First, agree with the sinner. There are too many hypocrites in the church. But there are also too many hypocrites running gas stations and managing grocery stores. Yet I still buy gas and get groceries. Always be truthful when dealing with the unsaved. Don't try to defend the hypocrites in the church. We all know they are there, and you will only prove your own hypocrisy if you try to cover up the truth. Here are the dynamite sticks for this excuse.

- Does the fact that there are hypocrites in the church excuse the sinner who is not in the church? ☐ Yes ☐ No

The point is, the sinner can answer only for himself, and we are not talking about church membership. We are talking about getting saved.

- What good does it do to judge another person? Will it help you? What does Romans 14:12 say about our judgment? ________________________________

  ____

  ____

- Where do all hypocrites go according to Matthew 24:51?

  ____

  ____

- How can you use this verse with a person who uses hypocrites as his excuse?

  ____

  ____

  ____

"I'm Afraid I Can't Hold Out" or "I Can't Live It"

Once more, agree with the sinner. No one can live the Christian life or keep God's Word. That's the very reason we need to be saved. Second Timothy 1:12 is dynamite sticks for this excuse.

- Who does the keeping? ________________
- What do we do? ____
  ____
- Is God able to keep us? ☐ Yes ☐ No
- Does God ever do anything halfway and then quit? ☐ Yes ☐ No
- Of what was Paul confident? ____
  ____
  ____
- If God cannot keep me saved, what does that say about His power?
  ____
  ____

"It Doesn't Make Much Difference What a Man Believes as Long as He Is Sincere"

This is a smokescreen used by the sinner to hide his own guilt and sin. Show him the folly of this statement by the experiences of the following three men.

Cain (Gen. 4:1-5)

- What clues do we see in this passage of Cain's sincere expectation that God would accept his offering? ________________________________
  ____
  ____
- Did Cain's sincerity help him? ☐ Yes ☐ No

- According to Hebrews 11:4, why did God accept Abel's offering, but not Cain's? ____
  ____

Ethiopian Eunuch (Acts 8:26-35)

- Was this man religious? ☐ Yes ☐ No
- Why had he been to Jerusalem? ____________________
- Did he read the Bible? ☐ Yes ☐ No
- Was he saved or lost before Philip witnessed to him? ________________

Religious and sincere as he was, he was still lost.

Cornelius (Acts 10:1-2, 44-48)

Name four good things about this man according to verse 2.

1. He was d__________.
2. He f__________ God.
3. He g______ alms or money to people.
4. He p__________ to God always.
   - Was he saved? ☐ Yes ☐ No
   - When did he get saved? ______________________________________
     ____
   - What did he do to get saved? ______________________________
     ____

He was devout, religious, sincere...but lost.

A good illustration can be made of a nurse who in all sincerity gives a child medicine for an illness. But the bottle, wrongly labeled, is poison and kills the child. She was sincere, but sincerely wrong.

"There Are Things I Can't Give Up"

This excuse is not often expressed but many times lies at the back of the sinner's thinking. The real problem is that he is not yet under enough conviction to give up everything for the Lord. You must be wise enough to detect this problem and address yourself to it.

Luke 18:18-23

- In your own words, describe what one thing the rich young ruler lacked.

  ____

  ____

  ____

- Why did the rich young ruler not follow Christ?

  ____

  ____

Don't make the mistake of trying to eliminate everything you think might keep the lost from saying, "Yes." In doing so, you might eliminate one of the most important and essential elements in salvation—repentance.

- What is repentance? ______________________________

  ____

We must make the plan of salvation as simple as possible, but never easier than God has made it.

Acts 17:30, 26:20

- What was Paul's message to the Gentiles (Acts 26:20)?

  ____

  ____

- What has God commanded in Acts 17:30?

  ____

  ____

2 Peter 3:9

- What is God's will according to 2 Peter 3:9?

  ____

  ____

  ____

A man who is not willing to give up his sin, who is not sick of his sin, and who does not hate his sin is not ready to repent. Only the Spirit can work repentance in his heart. Don't make it easy on the sinner by saying, "Don't worry about your sin; you can worry about that when you get saved!" Sin must be uppermost in the mind of the sinner at the moment of conversion. He must face his sin, hate it, and by faith turn to the blood of Christ for cleansing from his sin.

BEHAVIOR

DAILY LIVING

Man's daily activity testifies to the fact that he's alive. Whether he is eating, working, playing, or just talking with others, the physical life is evident. The Christian's daily activity also testifies to the fact that he is alive spiritually. Whether he is eating, working, playing, or talking with others, the Christian wants his life to glorify Christ (1 Cor. 10:31). The Christian's spiritual life is evident in the fact that he delights in God and depends on Him with all his heart. This delight and dependence bears fruit in the form of spiritual diligence and practicing the spiritual disciplines. As man's conduct testifies that he is alive, so the Christian's behavior testifies that he is in contact with the very source of life—God Himself.

THE GOD OF DELIGHT

TEACHER'S LESSON

- ***God as Joyful*** ______________
    - The __________ loves the _____
    - The _____ loves the __________
    - The __________ communicates the love between the Father and Son
    - The Godhead is an overflowing _____________ of ____________
- ***God as Joyful*** ______________
    - God created everything to ____________ His glory
    - God created everything to ___________________ His love
    - God created everything to ____________ your heart
    - God created everything because He is the overflowing _____________ of ____________
- ***God as Joyful*** ____________
    - Man's rebellion _________________ God and __________ His people
    - Christ's coming to ________ magnifies God and delights His people
    - Christ's coming to _______ magnifies God and delights His people

WORD POWER

- ***Delight***—take great joy or pleasure in something
- ***Glory***—the excellencies or perfections of God
- ***Trinity***—the doctrine that the one true God exists as three coequal persons
- ***Glorify***—to declare the perfections and value of God

STUDENT'S LESSON

Your student's lesson this week will trace the theme of God's glory through the Bible's storyline. God has been busy from even before "the beginning." He has been at work magnifying His glory, to exalt what is supremely valuable—Himself.

As we learned in the teacher's lesson this week, there is nothing more loving or delightful than to see and know more of our wonderful God. God isn't just working out His own glory; He is also enabling the only way you will ever be truly and supremely happy. If God isn't magnified, you will not be satisfied. He is at work for His glory and your joy!

As you read the following passages, remember that God's "name" is another way of talking about His character or reputation. (For a fuller discussion of these verses see Appendix 1 in John Piper's *Desiring God*, pages 255-66.)

Old Testament

Read the following passages from the Old Testament and answer the questions. Observe God's purpose in working in each of these situations.

Genesis 11:1-10

- Why did the makers of the tower of Babel want to build a structure that reached to the heavens? ____

  ____
- In stopping their building efforts, whose glory (name) was God protecting?

  ____

Ezekiel 20:5-9

- This passage is discussing the exodus from Egypt. Why did God deliver His people from slavery to the Egyptians?

  ____

Psalm 106:6-8

- What does verse 8 say about God's reason for freeing His people from Egypt? He did it ____

  ____ .

Exodus 14:4, 18

- What do these verses say that God was doing to (or over) Pharoah, the king of Egypt, when He delivered His people from Egypt?

  ____

  ____

Ezekiel 20:21-22

- This passage deals with Israel's wandering in the wilderness. What reason does God give for being merciful to His people in the wilderness, even though they sinned against Him repeatedly?

  ____

  ____

2 Samuel 7:23

- What does David say was God's motivation in giving His people victory over the Canaanites when they were conquering the land under Joshua's leadership? ____

  ____

1 Samuel 12:19-23

- Why did God not destroy His people when they sinned against Him by taking a census of the people? ____

  ____

1 Kings 8:41-45

- Why did God have Solomon build the temple? ____________________
- What did God say would happen to the non-Israelite nations when they observed His people worshiping at the temple? ____________________

  ____

Isaiah 48:9-11

- What does the prophet Isaiah say was the reason that God was going to show mercy to His people who had rebelled and been sent away into Babylon?

  ____

  ____

New Testament

Read the following passages from the New Testament and answer the questions. Consider what the passages reveal about God's plan in sending Christ to the earth and God's ultimate purpose for every believer both now and throughout eternity.

John 17:4

- What did Christ's works on earth (miracles, healings, etc.) accomplish in God's plan? ______________________________

John 12:27-28

- On the night before His crucifixion, what did the Father tell His Son that He would accomplish on the cross? ______________________________

  ____

1 Corinthians 10:31

- What does Paul say the goal of every aspect of the Christian life should be?

  ____

  ____

2 Thessalonians 1:9-10

- What does Paul say will happen to the Lord when He comes back again in the future? ______________________________

  ____

Revelation 21:23

- What will light up heaven for all eternity? ______________________________

  ____

Conclusion

- What do these verses teach us about God's priorities in all He does?

  ____

- What are the most important things in your life? What are you passionate about?

  ____

  ____

- How do the priorities of your life match up with the priorities of God?

  ____

  ____

  ____

THE DUTY OF DELIGHT

TEACHER'S LESSON

- ________________ ***to Delight***
    - You are commanded to delight in ________________
    - You are commanded to delight through God's ________
    - You are commanded to delight through God's __________
- ________________ ***with Delight***
    - When God says "Delight in Me," isn't He being ______________ ?
        - Answer: ____
          ____
    - How can God command me to produce an ______________?
        - Answer: ____
          ____
    - If delighting in God is the most wonderful experience possible, isn't focusing on my delight in Him a bit ______________?
        - Answer: ____
          ____

WORD POWER

- *Command*—instruction from the Lord that must be obeyed
- *Emotions*—the inner aspect of human beings that experiences feelings

STUDENT'S LESSON

Last week, we learned that God is the overflowing fountain of delight. We've seen that God is most delighted in what is most delightful—God! He delights in Himself, as He overflows into creation and salvation. This week we are learning that God expects and commands us also to delight in Him.

Objects of Delight and Joy

The following passages talk about a believer's delight. Look up each verse and write in the blank what or who should be the object of our delight. What should you take joy in?

- Psalm 43:4 ____________________
- John 16:22 ____________________
- Romans 5:11 ____________________
- Romans 14:17 ____________________
- Philippians 4:4 ____________________

Commands of Emotion

What emotions do the following passages command that a Christian have in his life?

- Psalm 42:5 ____________________
- Psalm 51:17 ____________________
- Luke 12:5 ____________________
- Romans 12:11 ____________________
- Ephesians 4:32 ____________________
- Ephesians 5:20 ____________________
- Philippians 2:3 ____________________
- Colossians 3:15 ____________________
- 1 Thessalonians 5:16 ____________________
- James 4:9 ____________________
- 1 Peter 2:2 ____________________

Works of Delight

As we are learning in this week's lesson, one way to begin rejoicing and delighting in God is to see and enjoy His works. The following passages give reasons for delight rooted in God's works for you. God has taken action for you, so you should delight in Him (through His works). Look up the passages below and write down what work of God is given that you can rejoice in. Then use the blank lines to explain how you can rejoice in God Himself through this particular work He has done for you.

- Deuteronomy 12:7 ______________________________
  - ______________________________
    ____
- Psalm 13:5 ______________________________
  - ______________________________
    ____
- Psalm 28:7 ______________________________
  - ______________________________
    ____
- Psalm 31:7 ______________________________
  - ______________________________
    ____
- Psalm 67:4 ______________________________
  - ______________________________
    ____
- Psalm 126:3 ______________________________
  - ______________________________
    ____
- Jeremiah 15:16 ______________________________
  - ______________________________
    ____

- Zechariah 2:10 ____

- ____
____

Project

Following the headings of our lesson for this week, make a list of thirty ways you can delight in God. The list should include ten items for each of the following categories: things about the character of God in which I can delight, truths from the Word of God in which I can delight, and works of God (past or present) in which I can delight. Give some thought to this project and be specific in your answers.

L E S S O N 3 0

DEPENDING ON THE GOSPEL

TEACHER'S LESSON

- ***God Is ________________ When We Depend on Him for ________________***
    - God is glorified in salvation _________
        - This happens _______ in the _________
    - God is glorified in salvation _______________
        - This happens _________ as we seek to _______ the Christian life
    - God is glorified in salvation _____________
        - This happens in the ___________ with results lasting for ________________
- ***God Is ________________ When We Depend on Him for ______________________________ (Growth)***
    - To grow, Christians need to ________ the gospel
    - To grow, Christians need to _________ with the gospel
    - To grow, Christians need to _______________ with the gospel
    - To grow, Christians need to _________ the gospel

WORD POWER

- ***Gospel***—the great message that God has provided a Redeemer in His Son Jesus Christ, who died for our sin and rose again according to the Scriptures
- ***Dependence***—complete reliance on God and the gospel
- ***Sanctification***—daily Christian growth by which a person becomes more like Christ

- *Conversion*—the point when a person first turned from his sin (repentance) and turned to Christ (faith) for salvation

STUDENT'S LESSON

God and Gospel-centered Living

In this lesson we are learning that the grace that saves you is that grace that changes you. By reminding yourself daily with what you know is real, you will grow as God designed. If you want to be fruitful, you've got to sink your roots deep into the reality of what God has done for you through Jesus Christ. In other words, you want God and His gospel to be at the center of your life, giving nutrients to strengthen your daily walk.

Here's a helpful illustration to help you think through how you can live a gospel-centered (or God-centered) life.

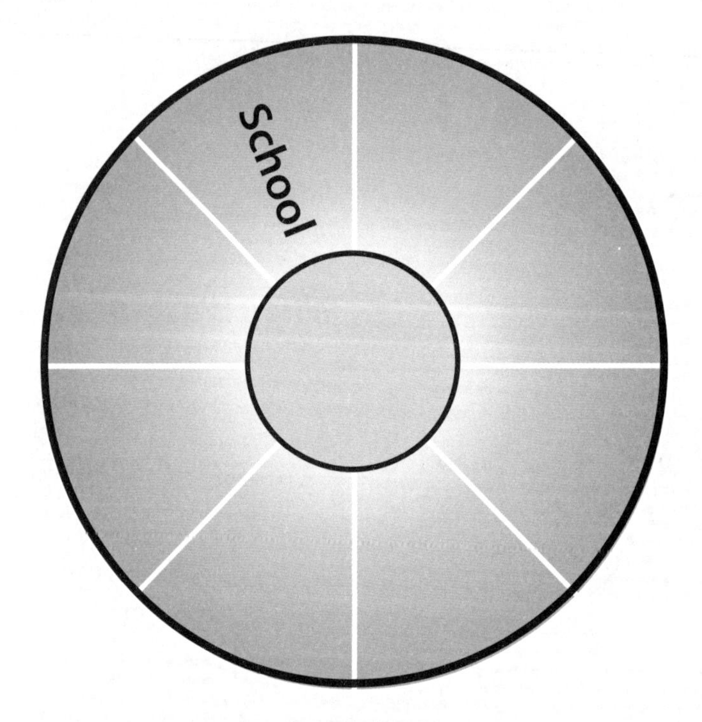

Fill in the pieces of the pie with different aspects of your life. For example, a first category is already written down for you: school. Fill in the other pie pieces with other categories that are an important part of your life. Let this pie reflect your interests.

When you're done, let's try an experiment. What would happen if one of your categories was at the center of pie, at the hub? In this spot, it became the most important area of life. Everything else around it, all the other categories, would take second place or be affected by what was in the center.

For example, if sports were at the center, how would that affect your school work? Perhaps, you'd start getting worse grades. Or perhaps you'd start working really hard to get good grades (so you wouldn't get kicked off the team), but you may let your kindness to your family suffer instead. You could be rude to them when they asked you to do things around the house. Get the picture? Great. Now it's your turn.

- Which area tends to be at the center of your life? How does it affect all the other areas? Fill in the blanks below.______________________________

- Now, let's try this again only with the right thing in the center. Go back and put God at the center of your pie. How would putting God at the center affect each of the other areas of your life? Take your time and prayerfully think through each answer.

God and Gospel-centered Reading

God's Word teaches us all about what God has done for us in the gospel. To learn and grow and thrive in the gospel, you've got to know what the Bible says. Read the following passages and write down in your own words all that you see the Bible saying that God has done for you in the gospel (because of what Christ has done).

- Romans 8:31-34 ______________________________

- Isaiah 53:3-6 ______________________________

- Romans 5:6-10 ______________________________

- 2 Corinthians 5:21 ______________________________

God and Gospel-centered Praying

Take one of the passages you've studied above and use that as a springboard to spend some time in prayer to God. Thank Him specifically for what He has already done. Praise Him for what He has promised to do for you in the future. Ask Him to open your eyes and help you see and savor each particular truth more fully. Ask Him to change you to reflect these truths in your life. Take at least five minutes in prayer working through the Scriptures and turning what you read into prayers to God.

DEPENDING ON GOD'S PROMISES

TEACHER'S LESSON

- ***Unmasking Sin's Promises***
  - Sin's promises are ________________
  - Sin's promises are ____________________
  - Sin's promises are not to be ____________
- ***Depending on God's Promises***
  - God always provides a ___________ promise
  - God's promises always have _______________________
  - Belief in God's promise is the __________ of every struggle
- ***Examples of Depending on God's Promises***
  - Depending on God's promises to fight ___________
    - Sin's promise: ____________________________________
      ____
    - God's promise: ___________________________________
      ____
  - Depending on God's promises to fight _________
    - Sin's promise: ____________________________________
      ____
    - God's promise: ___________________________________
      ____

- Depending on God's promises to fight ________
  - Sin's promise: ____
    ____
  - God's promise: ____
    ____

WORD POWER

- *Promise*—a pledge that someone gives that he will do what he says
- *Temptation*—an allurement to do evil; a test of your love and loyalty to God
- *Lust*—a strong desire
- *Idol*—something other than God that you depend on to help make life work

STUDENT'S LESSON

This lesson has focused on how we fight sin. We don't simply say "No" to sin. We, by faith, believe that God's promises to us are better and will make us happier than giving in to sin. Sin's promises never really satisfy. In this student's lesson, you will look more fully into what sin's promises are really like and what God's promises are really like. You can be confident that sin cannot keep its promises, but God always will.

The Nature of Sin's Promises

Read Psalm 115:1-9. This passage gives a vivid contrast. On the one hand is the true God, who can truly help His people. On the other hand are the idols that people have made that can't help anyone. In fact, they need help themselves.

People in Bible times often looked to false gods or idols to provide for them, to protect them, and to make life work. But they had put their trust in little hunks of wood or metal that couldn't do anything for them. Whatever the people had thought these idols had promised them wasn't going to happen. These idols couldn't deliver on any promise.

According to Psalm 115:4-7, write down at least seven different ways that these idols are limited.

- What are these idols really like?____

These idols looked like they could see, hear, feel, and speak. But they couldn't do any of that!

- How are sin's promises the same?

- Read Psalm 115:8. If you start believing sin's promises, what will giving in to temptation do to you as a person?

- Read Psalm 115:4. Why is it that these idols (and any sin) cannot deliver what they promise? What is the core problem?

No sin or temptation is as powerful as God. They don't have the ability to deliver anything worthwhile. Only God, the powerful Creator, can make good on His promises.

So, let's turn from sin's weak promises to God's mighty promises.

The Nature of God's Promises

Read Romans 4:16-25.

- According to Romans 4:18, what had God promised to Sarah and Abraham?

- According to Romans 4:19, what appeared to be obstacles to God's keeping His promise? List at least two.

- According to Romans 4:20, how did these "obstacles" affect Abraham's faith in God's promise? Restate the entire verse in your own words. ______________

____

____

____

____

- Read Romans 4:16-25 again. What verse gives two truths about God and His ability to do the impossible? What are the two truths? ______________

____

____

____

- Write a paragraph contrasting the false idols (in Ps. 115:1-9) and the true God (in Rom. 4:16-25). ______________________________

____

____

____

____

Project on God's Promises

1. Identify one specific sin that someone your age may struggle with.

____

2. Think through and write down three or more lies this sin promises. What does this sin or temptation want people to believe that it can give? ______________

____

____

____

____

3. List from the Bible three better promises God makes to those who obey Him and don't give in to temptation? In other words, what promises from God should a person believe instead of sin's promises? ______________________

____

____

____

____

____

(Hint: you may want to use a Bible dictionary to look up the particular sin you may be struggling with. It will give you ideas about what the Bible says about this sin and God's right way to live.)

LIVING THE CHRISTIAN FAITH WITH DILIGENCE

TEACHER'S LESSON

- ***Faith*** __________
    - You need to let ______ do the work
    - You need to ______________ your ________ to obey
    - You need to be __________________ on God and be ________________ yourself
    - Your ____________________ demonstrates itself through your __________________
        - Dependence ___________________ diligence
        - Diligence _________________ dependence
- ***Faith*** ______________
    - Know your __________
    - Never ________________

WORD POWER

- *Diligence*—disciplined activity
- *Canaan*—the land which God promised to His people in the Old Testament

STUDENT'S LESSON

This week's lesson looked at how you need to be diligent in your Christian life. Effort, spiritual "sweat," and hard work are part of the Christian's experience. But why should we fight Satan? Hasn't he already been defeated (Heb. 2:14)? Do we really need to fight against sin? Aren't we all going to make it to heaven anyway? Since Christ already paid for our sin, does it really matter that we fight against sin?

Lessons from Old Testament Warfare

When Joshua led the children of Israel into the Promised Land (Canaan), they were headed for a battle. They were going to drive out the pagan nations that lived there and claim the land God had promised them.

As the army of Israel marched through the land, God continued to encourage them. What do you think He told them? Did He say, "Keep up the good work," or "Don't quit fighting hard, or you'll never win the land"?

- Read Joshua 1:2-3; 6:2-3; 8:1; 8:18; and Judges 1:2. In the blanks provided write down in your own words what God told Israel as they headed into battle.

  ____

  ____

  ____

  ____

  ____

- Who was going to win the fight? Who was going to take the land? Israel or God?

  ____

- Now go back and re-read the verses listed above. Write down in the blanks provided below the human action or commands that went along with God's promise to give Israel the land. ______________________________

  ____

  ____

  ____

  ____

- Who actually went onto the battlefield and fought against the pagan nations of Canaan? Israel or God? ________________

- What motivated and encouraged the Israelites as they went into battle? ____
____
____

- Did Israel sit back and wait for God to take action and destroy the enemy for them? ☐ Yes ☐ No

- How did Israel respond to the promises God had made to give them the land of Canaan? ____
____

- What did the Israelites' actions (going into battle) say about their belief in God's promises to give them the land? ________________________________
____

- If Israel had said, "God, thanks for promising to give us the land. We'll sit here and watch You do it because we know You can't go back on Your promise," would they be demonstrating belief in God's promise or unbelief? ______________

- When God says to you, "I will protect you spiritually, I will keep you from Satan's destruction, and I've already dealt with all of your sin," does that mean that you don't have to work hard and fight spiritually against sin and Satan? ☐ Yes ☐ No

Lessons from Old Testament Heroes

The Old Testament is full of other examples of faith in action. Read the following passages. Each one talks about an Old Testament character's faith and then what that person did—how he or she acted and lived—because of that faith. Write out in the blanks provided what actions each person did because of their faith in God and His promises.

- Hebrews 11:4 ____
____

- Hebrews 11:7 ____

____

- Hebrews 11:8-9 ____

____

- Hebrews 11:17 ____

____

- Hebrews 11:20 ____

____

- Hebrews 11:21 ____

____

- Hebrews 11:22 ____

____

- Hebrews 11:24-28 ____

____

____

____

____

____

- Hebrews 11:29 ____

____

Each person's faith spurred them on to more obedience and diligent action for God. You should diligently work out your faith.

Lessons from New Testament Application

For each of the references given, fill in the adjacent columns. Look for what is true that God wants you to believe by faith (dependence). Then look for what God wants you to do in action (diligence).

	What Is True (Dependence)	*What to Do (Diligence)*
Romans 13:12-14		
Romans 14:12-13		
1 Corinthians 6:20		
1 Corinthians 9:24-27		
1 Corinthians 10:13-14		
Galatians 5:1		
Ephesians 4:32		
Ephesians 5:8 (cf. 5:5-7)		
Colossians 2:6		

For the Christian, life is always believing more of what Christ has done for us and has promised to do for us. It is also diligently applying that faith to life-actions. In the blanks below, write down your own personal and specific applications for each of the passages above. Don't just write down exactly what the verse says. Go further than that and ask

God to help you identify specific areas where your faith needs to take action, where you need to be diligent by faith.

	What to Do (Diligence)—Your Own Application!
Romans 13:12-14	
Romans 14:12-13	
1 Corinthians 6:20	
1 Corinthians 9:24-27	
1 Corinthians 10:13-14	
Galatians 5:1	
Ephesians 4:32	
Ephesians 5:8 (cf. 5:5-7)	
Colossians 2:6	

131

RUNNING THE CHRISTIAN RACE WITH DILIGENCE

TEACHER'S LESSON

- ***Faith*** ________
  - Faith runs with __________
    - Run after _________________
    - Run after _______________________
  - Faith runs with ____________
  - Faith runs with __________
    - Lay aside _____________________________
    - Lay aside ___________________
    - Lay aside _____
  - Faith runs with __________________
- ***Faith*** ________

WORD POWER

- *Faith*—reliance on God and all He has promised in the gospel of Jesus Christ
- *Godliness*—a God-orientation to all of life
- *Assurance*—the God-given confidence that you are His child
- *Endurance*—sustained strength for continued action

STUDENT'S LESSON

We've been learning how important it is to run the Christian race with diligence. The New Testament teaches that a true Christian will never quit the race. He may stop for a while, but he'll always get back into the race.

This is a great place to stop and remind ourselves about how God has promised that none of His children will lose the race. If you are His child running the race, He has promised to make sure you finish successfully. In this student's lesson, we're going to look at several of God's promises related to the security of your salvation.

In the Bible God has made some promises (read Heb. 10:23). He has obligated Himself in writing. He gives you His word that He will do particular things when you come to Him in faith. If you've not been running well and are doubting that you might really be a Christian, or if you know someone who is struggling with assurance, these verses are a great place to start.

God's purpose in giving you assurance of finishing the race is not to produce lazy runners. They might say, "I know that I'll finish. God has told me that I would. So, I can just ease up and take a break." This type of thinking is unbiblical. Instead, God intends these words of assurance to give you more energy to finish strong. If someone told you that in 10 years you would be the world's best athlete if you practiced, how would that make you practice? With energy and focus, or with laziness and carelessness?

Let's dig into God's Word looking for His promises of assurance that He owns us and that we will finish the race. Look up the following verses and write them out in your own words in the space provided. Then answer the questions related to each passage.

John 5:24 ____

____

____

- What do you have to do to receive the promises God makes in this verse?

  ____

- What are the promises God makes to those who rely on Him?

  ____

  ____

  ____

  ____

John 6:37 ______________________________

____

____

- What is true about the people who will come to Christ for salvation? Who are they? ______________________________

  ____

- How will Christ treat the people who come to Him for salvation?

  ____

  ____

- Have you come to Christ for salvation? ☐ Yes ☐ No

- Are you continuing to rely on Christ alone as your Rescuer from sin?
  ☐ Yes ☐ No

- What does this verse teach you about what really caused you to come to Christ in the first place? ______________________________

  ____

- What promises do verses 39-40 make concerning those who believe in Christ?

  ____

  ____

  ____

- Re-read John 6:37 and also read John 10:28-29. If you have come to Christ because the Father gave you to Him, will Christ ever let you wander away from His fold?

  ____

  ____

Psalm 147:11 ______________________________

____

____

- What kind of people bring delight or pleasure to God? ______________________________

  ____

  ____

- Where do you see God's steadfast or merciful love clearly demonstrated?

____

____

- When you rely on Christ's rescue, how does that make God feel?

____

- If you really wonder whether God accepts your faith in Christ, how does this uncertainty make God feel? ______________________

____

____

____

1 Corinthians 1:8 ______________________________

____

____

- According to 1 Corinthians 7b-8, who will establish you as blameless (verify that you pass His inspection) on the day of God's judgment?

____

____

- Who will ultimately see to it that you finish your race? ______________

2 Timothy 2:13 ______________________________

____

____

- What is God's response to you when you are not living faithfully to Him (when you are not pursuing godliness)? ______________________

____

- Why does God remain faithful to us even when we are unfaithful?

____

____

Romans 8:29-30 ______________________________

____

____

When you trusted Christ as your Rescuer from sin, you were justified. In other words, when you became a Christian, God declared you as completely righteous in His sight.

- What does this passage teach will happen to those who are justified?

  ____

- Does this passage say that some of those who are justified will be glorified?
  ☐ Yes ☐ No
- Will there be anyone who trusts in Christ and is justified who will not be glorified? ☐ Yes ☐ No

Psalm 34:22 (also read 2 Sam. 22:31) ______________________________

____

____

- What does God promise will not happen to you if you are taking refuge (relying on) Him? ______________________________

  ____

- Will there be any people who are taking refuge in God who might somehow face His judgment? ☐ Yes ☐ No

Listen to the words of one pastor who had struggled with enjoying his salvation. Here is how he preached the gospel to himself, to remind himself that he couldn't base his assurance on his feelings or on his Christian performance. This pastor, Martin Luther, said to himself, "Flesh and Satan, you are lying; for God has spoken and has made a promise. He will not lie, even if the opposite happens or I die in the meantime."

And here is Martin Luther's similar advice to you, when you are struggling with doubt, fear, and assurance. He says, "So when the Devil throws your sins in your face, and declares that you deserve death and hell, tell him this: I admit that I deserve death and hell. What of it? For I know one who suffered and made satisfaction in my behalf. His name is Jesus Christ, the Son of God. Where He is, there I shall be also!"

INTRODUCING THE SPIRITUAL DISCIPLINES

TEACHER'S LESSON

- ***The ______________ of the Spiritual Disciplines***
  - The spiritual disciplines are like a __________________________
  - The spiritual disciplines don't ___________________ godliness
  - The spiritual disciplines help you draw on God's __________
- ***The ____________ of Spiritual Disciplines***
  - Spiritual disciplines are valuable because ____________ __________________ them in Scripture
  - Spiritual disciplines are valuable because they put you in contact with _____________________
  - Spiritual disciplines are valuable because they put you in contact with ____
- ***The _________________ of the Spiritual Disciplines***
  - Beware of spiritual _______________
  - Beware of spiritual __________________________
  - Beware of spiritual __________
  - Beware of spiritual _____________________

WORD POWER

- *Spiritual Disciplines*—various spiritual exercises which promote godliness
- *Fellowship*—a relationship among Christians aimed at mutual encouragement

STUDENT'S LESSON

It's time to start your practice of the spiritual disciplines, and, like physical exercise, it's good to start small. No one runs a marathon his first day of running. Start with small goals and build from there.

Start with a Verse

We'll learn more about the specific spiritual disciplines in the next lesson, but we'll focus on just a few important ones here. Turn in your Bible to Acts 2:41-42.

Write the Verse

- In your own words, write the text of these two verses.

  ____

  ____

  ____

  ____

Study the Verse

Now, answer the following questions about this passage.

- According to 2:41, who are the people doing spiritual activities in 2:42?

  ____

- According to 2:42, with what attitude did these people do the spiritual activities?

  ____

  ____

- Read Acts 2:46-47. How often do you think the believers were practicing these spiritual disciplines? ____________________________

- What are the four activities that the believers were practicing?

  ____

  ____

  ____

  ____

Apply the Verse

The following categories reflect the spiritual disciplines given in Acts 2:42. These are not the only spiritual disciplines, but they are a good, short list with which to begin. This is a great place to start your spiritual exercises. Let's get going.

Bible Teaching

- Write down the exact wording of the first spiritual discipline these earlier believers engaged in. ____________________

- Read Romans 1:1. Where today can you find the teaching of the apostles?

  ____

- What else did this early church enjoy from the apostles, according to Acts 2:43? ____________________

- Even though this early group of Christians could see and experience miraculous wonders from the hands of the apostles, they didn't give themselves to miracles. What, according to Acts 2:42, did these early Christians devote themselves to? ____________________

These believers gave themselves completely to learning God's Word. They committed and devoted themselves to it. This was no passing interest. It was part of their lives and their passion.

- List five specific ways you can begin devoting yourself to the Bible's teaching.

  ____

  ____

  ____

  ____

  ____

Fellowship

- What does Acts 2:42 list as the second spiritual discipline?

  ____

- What does this word bring to your mind? Describe and illustrate what this word usually looks like. ____

____

____

The word for "fellowship" means partnership. It has nothing to do with food or snacks after a church service. Fellowship is not even a Christian version of friendship.

Biblical fellowship is what you and another person have in common. If you are a Christian and someone else is a Christian, you are in fellowship. At first, it's not even something you do; it's something you are. You are in fellowship or partnership with all other Christians.

- Fellowship is also something you do. Because you and other Christians are partners, there is a sharing and helping of each other. Read Acts 2:44-45. What did this partnership (fellowship) actually look like between believers. List each element. ____

____

____

- Read Acts 4:32-37. List what the partnering (fellowshipping) looked like as described in these verses. Describe each aspect in detail.

____

____

____

____

____

- List five practical ways that you can demonstrate the loving and sacrificial partnership you have with other Christians. (Remember, this is a spiritual exercise that the early believers didn't just practice—they devoted themselves to it!)

____

____

____

____

____

Breaking Bread

- According to Acts 2:42, what is the third spiritual exercise that believers devoted themselves to? ____________________

- What do you think this means?____________________

  ____

This expression has been interpreted several different ways. But it seems clear that at least it means that the believers enjoyed time together over food. It may refer to taking the Lord's Supper (communion), or it may refer to simply eating meals together (read Acts 2:46). Either way, both events (communion or meals) are times of warm interaction with other believers.

Early Christians loved each other and loved spending time with each other. Have you ever thought about spending time with other Christians as a "spiritual discipline?"

It's easy to think about Christianity as a religion for the head. You have to learn a lot of stuff from the Bible. But Christianity has a lot to do with relationships. Time spent in loving relationship with other Christians is not wasted time.

- Read Ephesians 5:29-30. How does Paul describe the church? What image or word picture does he use? ____________________

- List at least 5 ways that this word picture teaches that Christians should spend time together regularly. ____________________

  ____

  ____

  ____

  ____

- List five ways you could simply enjoy time together with other Christians, explaining how each could benefit you spiritually.

  ____

  ____

  ____

  ____

  ____

- What is the last spiritual discipline in Acts 2:42? ____________________

The original word for "prayer" in the Greek is actually plural, and can be translated "the prayers." It seems that these early Christians (most of whom were converted Jews) continued to meet in the temple for the regularly scheduled prayer times. Read Acts 2:46. The prayers these believers prayed, were at specific times. They prayed "the prayers."

- What kind of official prayer time do Christians have together today? List a few examples.____

  ____

When the church body gathers together for weekly services, one thing they do together is pray. It is very important to exercise the spiritual discipline of prayer both on your own and when you meet with your church family. These believers devoted themselves to praying together.

- Write down three words that would accurately describe your spiritual discipline of prayer.____

  ____

- What are five practical steps you can take to devote yourself to the spiritual discipline of prayer?

  ____

  ____

  ____

  ____

  ____

- List three ways that you can bring other Christians along with you. Your practice of the spiritual disciplines with others could be a real help and blessing to you and to them.

  ____

  ____

  ____

Conclusion

As we have been studying the spiritual disciplines, you have four good exercises to start with. On a separate sheet of paper, write a one-paragraph description of how God has been speaking to you about your need to practice the spiritual disciplines. Then write out a detailed action plan of how you can begin your regular practice of spiritual exercises. Use the steps below to help you prepare your action plan.

1. Prayerfully pick two spiritual disciplines that you would like to add to your life on a more regular basis.
2. For each discipline write out a verse of Scripture that shows the importance of that spiritual discipline. Then record specifically why you want to grow in that area.
3. For each discipline write out specific times and places that you intend to practice the spiritual discipline.
4. For each discipline write out three or more things that could hinder you from being faithful in practicing the spiritual discipline.
5. Find a friend, parent, or other mature believer to keep you accountable for practicing what you have recorded.
6. Pray daily for God's grace to enable you to develop these spiritual disciplines in your life.

PRACTICING THE SPIRITUAL DISCIPLINES

TEACHER'S LESSON

- ***Disciplines of the Word***
  - ______________ the Word of God
    - The Bible instructs us to take in the Word of God by hearing it ________
    - The Bible instructs us to take in the Word of God by hearing it ____________________
    - The Bible instructs us to hear the Word of God through the __________________________ in church
  - _______________ the Word of God
    - Biblical examples of examining the Word of God
      - _________________________, __________, and ___________
    - Practical advice on examining the Word of God
      - Take in the Bible ____
      - Take in the Bible with a _______ in mind
      - Take in the Bible with helpful and simple ____________________
      - Take in the Bible to make it ________________________________
  - _________________ the Word of God
    - God's Word is a ____________ to be kept and protected in our hearts
    - Have a ________ to memorize God's Word
    - Use creative methods to memorize God's Word
    - Remember a ________________ as you memorize God's Word

- ________________ on the Word of God
    - Meditate means to slowly chew on the Scriptures
    - Meditation chews on what ____________________ made available
    - You need both _____ and ____________________________ to understand His Word
    - Chewing on God's Word brings __________________________

- ***Discipline of*** ____
- ***Discipline of*** ____
- ***Discipline of*** ________________ ***and*** __________________
- ***Discipline of*** ________________
- ***Discipline of*** _______________________

WORD POWER

- *Meditate*—to consider the Scriptures slowly and thoughtfully
- *Journaling*—recording your thoughts in writing
- *Fasting*—to go without food (or something else) in order to focus on God

STUDENT'S LESSON

We have finally come to the end of our study of the basics of *Dynamic Christian Living*. You may be surprised at how much you have learned this year. To check up on how much you remember, work through the following multiple choice statements. Choose the best answer to complete each statement. Try to answer all the questions without looking back in your book. Then look up the answers for the ones about which you were unsure. How much will you remember?

____ 1. The word that means to liberate, deliver, heal, or set free is (a) redemption (b) salvation (c) reconciliation.

____ 2. Being "born again" or the new birth whereby we pass from death unto life is (a) regeneration (b) remission (c) justification.

____ 3. Being declared righteous in God's sight is
(a) redemption (b) remission (c) justification.

____ 4. The correct answer to the question, "What must I do to be saved?" is
(a) be baptized (b) believe on the Lord Jesus Christ (c) join the church.

____ 5. The correct order for the four steps that gave us our Bibles is
(a) inspiration, organization, collection, preservation
(b) organization, collection, inspiration, preservation
(c) collection, inspiration, organization, preservation.

____ 6. Part of the proof of the Bible's inspiration is that over (a) 30 (b) 100 (c) 300 Old Testament prophecies about the Messiah were fulfilled in Jesus Christ.

____ 7. The first five books of the Hebrew Bible is the section known as the
(a) prophets (b) law (c) writings.

____ 8. The list of books inspired by God that are the standard or rule by which we should govern our lives is the
(a) Canon (b) Apocrypha (c) Septuagint.

____ 9. The ancient book with the largest quantity of manuscript evidence is
(a) Homer's *Iliad* (b) the Old Testament (c) the New Testament.

____ 10. The symbol of the Bible that reminds us that it sustains life, growth, and fruit is (a) a mirror (b) a lamp (c) water.

____ 11. The symbol of the Bible that reminds us that it purifies the heart and life is (a) fire (b) a hammer (c) seed.

____ 12. The people in Acts 17 who did not accept what Paul said without studying the Scriptures for themselves were the
(a) Thessalonians (b) Bereans (c) Romans.

____ 13. The aspect of prayer by which we offer our requests to God is called
(a) confession (b) adoration (c) supplication.

____ 14. One of the things that the apostles regarded as among their most important activities was (a) feeding the hungry (b) taking care of the widows (c) prayer.

____ 15. According to Matthew 6:6, if we pray in secret, God will
(a) listen to our prayers (b) reward us openly (c) keep others from knowing what our requests are.

____ 16. The hindrance to answered prayer referred to in Psalm 66:18 is lack of
(a) purity (b) faith (c) love.

____ 17. According to John 15, believers are to abide in
(a) Christ (b) the Word of God (c) Christ and the Word of God.

____ 18. The purpose of the Lord's Model Prayer is to
(a) teach us how to pray (b) show us how Christ prayed
(c) show us how the disciples prayed.

____ 19. When we "hallow" God's name, that means we are
(a) talking about it to others (b) treating it with respect
(c) calling upon it for our needs.

____ 20. The petition concerning man in the Lord's Model Prayer that focuses on our moral needs is
(a) give us our bread (b) forgive us our debts (c) deliver us from evil.

____ 21. According to 1 Corinthians 6:19, after we are saved we become
(a) the temple of the Holy Spirit (b) ambassadors for Christ
(c) children of God.

____ 22. The first step in witnessing is
(a) arousing curiosity in spiritual things (b) making personal contact (c) communicating what Christ means to me.

____ 23. The verse that tells us that the gospel is the power of God unto salvation for all who believe is Romans (a) 1:16 (b) 3:23 (c) 10:9.

____ 24. In Revelation 20:11-15, the second death is when
(a) an unsaved man dies (b) the unsaved are raised from the dead and cast into the lake of fire (c) people are given a second chance after death to accept the Lord.

____ 25. The true meaning of Christ's death is that
(a) He died as man's substitute (b) His death was an accident
(c) He died as a martyr.

____ 26. The first part to clinching the decision is showing the man that
(a) he must pay for his sin (b) Christ died for his sin (c) he is a sinner.

____ 27. One way I should deal with the excuse "I have sinned too much" is by reminding the sinner
(a) don't wait for tomorrow (b) God saved the chief of sinners (c) the friends of the world are the enemies of God.

____ 28. Before creation, in what did God express His joy and delight?
(a) the thought of creation (b) His sovereign plan
(c) the members of the Godhead

____ 29. Where can you see and delight in God Himself?
(a) in people's hearts (b) in prayer (c) in His works

____ 30. Salvation refers to which kind of an event?
(a) past (b) present (c) future

____ 31. Ephesians 4:22 refers to our sinful desires as what?
(a) youthful (b) deceitful (c) strong

____ 32. Which is the best approach to Christian growth?
(a) you need to be dependent on God and be diligent yourself
(b) you need to make up your mind to obey (c) you need to let God do the work

____ 33. What is one of the goals of the Christian race?
(a) spiritual discipline (b) endurance (c) godliness

____ 34. Why are the spiritual disciplines valuable?
(a) they help you become more self-disciplined (b) they connect you to Scripture (c) they show someone is serious about their Christian life

____ 35. Which way to take in the Scriptures does the Bible not directly recommend?
(a) in song (b) in sermons (c) in good Christian books

RESOURCES FOR FURTHER STUDY

General

Elwell, Walter A. *Baker's Topical Guide to the Bible.*

Erickson, Millard. *The Concise Dictionary of Christian Theology.*

MacArthur, John. *The Keys to Spiritual Growth.*

Salvation

Bridges, Jerry. *The Gospel for Real Life.*

Packer, J. I. *Knowing God.*

Stott, John R. W. *Basic Christianity.*

Scripture

MacArthur, John. *Why Believe the Bible.*

Strobel, Lee. *The Case for Christ.*

Prayer

Carson, D. A. *A Call to Spiritual Reformation.*

MacArthur, John. *Alone with God: Rediscovering the Power and Passion of Prayer.*

Ryle, J. C. *A Call to Prayer.*

Witnessing

Dever, Mark. *The Gospel and Personal Evangelism.*

Stiles, Mack. *Speaking of Jesus.*

Daily Living

Berg, Jim. *Changed into His Image: Student Edition.*

Bunyan, John. *Pilgrim's Progress.*

Mahaney, C. J. *Living the Cross Centered Life.*

Piper, John. *Battling Unbelief: Defeating Sin with Superior Pleasure.*

Piper, John. *When I Don't Desire God.*